THE
SPENDTHRIFTS

BY

BENITO PEREZ GALDOS

WITH ILLUSTRATIONS
BY CHARLES MOZLEY
INTRODUCTION BY GERALD BRENAN

FARRAR STRAUS & YOUNG INC.
NEW YORK
1952

TRANSLATED FROM THE SPANISH
»LA DE BRINGAS«
BY GAMEL WOOLSEY

SET IN 12 POINT BEMBO
PRINTED BY BRÜDER ROSENBAUM
VIENNA, AUSTRIA

PEREZ GALDOS
THE SPENDTHRIFTS

———————————

THE
ILLUSTRATED NOVEL
LIBRARY

INTRODUCTION

It is a strange thing that, although Spain is a country which has always had a great attraction for English speaking people, Spanish novelists are very little known to them. Everyone, of course, has heard of Cervantes and many people have read Blasco Ibañez, but how many people know even the name of Pérez Galdós? Yet Galdós is not only the most popular of Spanish writers, whose books are a household word among his countrymen, but he is a major European novelist who ranks with Balzac, Dostoevsky and Dickens. He is unknown outside Spain and Latin America because none of his mature works have been translated.

There is not very much to be said about Galdós as a man. He was born in 1843 at Las Palmas in the Canary Islands of a prosperous middle class family, and went to school at an English college in that city. Here he learned our language well enough to read and fall in love with Dickens. We are told that he was a timid, silent youth, much given to reading, and, when he was nineteen, his parents sent him to Madrid to study law. Madrid was at this time in the full glamour of the late Isabelline period, pleasure-loving, animated and idle. From midday to midnight the streets and cafés were thronged with people: plots and revolutions were in the air, yet such was the mildness of the age that the fear and hatred which had been so prevalent thirty years earlier during the era of the Carlist Civil Wars had all been dissipated. The young Galdós threw himself into this pleasant life with zest. The theatres, the cafés, the *Ateneo*—Madrid's club for writers and politicians—and no doubt the usual love

7

affairs drank up the time he should have given to his law books. But he had private means, so that he did not need to work. He had fallen in love with Madrid, and he set himself to observe and study it.

He was not long in discovering his literary vocation. He started by writing plays and reporting for the daily papers, but in 1866 a visit to Paris and the reading of Balzac put him on the right track. His first novel, set in the Liberal revolutionary era of 1820–23, came out the following year. He had been led to this subject by a political motive. He wanted to discover the causes of the backwardness of his country, of its chaotic political regime, its poverty and its idleness. He believed that these lay a generation or more back in the struggle that had taken place between the Clericals and the Liberals. But one book on this subject was clearly not enough, so he embarked on a series of historical novels, known as the *National Episodes*, which began in 1805 with *Trafalgar* and eventually ended in the 1880's with *Cánovas*. This immense work, comprising forty-five separate volumes, he offered to his fellow countrymen as a living picture of their history.

But Galdós was not satisfied with writing on historical subjects. He had settled down in Madrid with a sister to keep house for him and before long his prodigious energy was being poured into a series of much fuller and richer novels upon contemporary life. Between 1876 and 1878, while still engaged on the *National Episodes*, he wrote four of these (the best is *Doña Perfecta*) and then, at the height of his powers, he wrote in quick succession the seven books on which his fame chiefly rests: *The Disinherited, Our Friend Manso, Tormento, The Spendthrifts, Miao, Fortunata and Jacinta* and *Angel Guerra*.

Such a prodigious output in twelve years exacts a penalty. After finishing *Angel Guerra* in 1891, Galdós had a nervous breakdown. Like Tolstoy, he came to think that nothing that he had hitherto written was of any value. He also felt that the Liberal ideas that had guided him were too superficial, and that what Spain needed was a religious reformation and a return to the social teaching of the New Testament. In this frame of mind he wrote *Nazarín*, a story of a priest who led an evangelic life of poverty in the slums, and *Misericordia*, a novel about beggars. These were the last of his novels on contemporary life. He regained his balance by forcing himself to return to his series of *National Episodes* and by writing plays. Then in 1912 his eyesight gave out. When he died eight years later he was blind.

As a person, Galdós eludes us. Reserved, shy and modest, he gives few clues of his inner life to his biographer. He avoided literary circles and was most at home with people of the lower middle class and with children. On his friends he made the impression of a rather shabby and hard worked family doctor, and everyone agreed that his most salient trait was his lack of egoism. He felt through the medium of other people and thus, like George Eliot, only revealed himself in his books.

We may call Galdós a novelist of the school of Balzac. He wrote soberly and objectively about the world as he saw it and did not associate himself with any of his characters. But to the Frenchman's rather colourless narrative he adds the warmth, humour and melodramatic sense of Dickens and the ironic wit and detachment of Cervantes. Further he is one of the great psychological novelists, endlessly curious about the varieties of human conduct and character. His books abound in abnormal types, religious maniacs and people on the border line of insanity, and as he grew older he tended to fill in much of the background of his novels with them. He shows an intuitive understanding of their case histories, which one can only compare with that shewn by Dostoevsky, though his approach is far more objective and clinical. Yet no one has ever written better than he does about the ordinary and the normal.

Fundamentally, however, his attitude to the world is that of a moralist. The plots of his books nearly always consist in his taking a man or woman who has a particular vice or weakness and showing how this weakness leads to his downfall. A man's fate, he believes, is the result of the working out of his character, and the slow and inevitable ruin of the hero and his vain struggles to escape from it give his novels an inner strength and consistency. But while no weakness escapes his eye, he is very tolerant. If, as William Blake said, the artist is the eternal forgiver of sins, then Galdós is one indeed. He forgives because he understands all the particulars of the case and because, when one understands these, one must forgive everyone or no one. The only people excluded from his compassion are those who have no heart, and who lack therefore the organs to which such a sentiment can be applied. And then if, as he believes, it is society that shapes men, how can one expect them in bad societies to behave well? Under Galdós's skin there was both a Christian who gave absolution and a Marxist who attributed the sins of the children to the fathers.

We have said that Galdós was a novelist of the school of Balzac. He takes human nature as he finds it and his characters are a sample of ordinary life. But how wonderfully vivid and well-defined they are! The bores, the shrews, the pompous, the nonentities are a perpetual delight when one meets them in his pages, the queer or mad provide melodrama and the more presentable characters give rise, as they should, to mixed feelings. One takes a bath in human nature when one reads Galdós, and comes out the better and the wiser for it.

He is especially good on family life. No novelist, I think, has ever described so well the intimate relations of married people, their little quarrels and differences, the part played by their children and by their relations and friends. In reading his books, one is never far away from the sewing and the ironing, the housekeeping and the weekly budget, and these things are brought in with admirable dramatic and comic effect. How is it, one asks, that a life-long bachelor could present so brilliantly the comedy of married life with all its humdrum incidents and fluctuations of feeling?

• The novel translated here as *The Spendthrifts* (its Spanish title is *La de Bringas*) is an excellent example of this. The scene is laid in the Royal Palace of Madrid, where the Bringas couple hold minor posts at the court of Queen Isabella. Bringas and his friend Pez are types of the upper and lower court bureaucracy, while Rosalía Bringas, who in other circumstances would be a model wife, is shown as a woman whose passion for dress is leading her into expenses that are far beyond her means. The comedy of the situation lies in the fact that her husband, whom in her own selfish way she loves and respects, is one of those model bureaucrats for whom extravagance is the worst of all crimes. The tragedy lies in the sufferings of Rosalía, who, driven on by her mania, sinks steadily deeper into debt and is obliged to resort to more and more precarious devices to conceal her extravagance from her husband.

But Rosalía is not the only woman in the Palace who is ruining herself in this way. Her friend, the Marquesa de Tellería, is in a similar plight, while in Doña Cándida, that superb parasite and bore, we get a portrait of an older woman who has reached the end of the same downward path. The rottenness of the whole regime becomes apparent and when, at the close of the sweltering summer, the Army, the Navy and the entire country rise with one

11

accord and the Queen flees to France, the curtain falls on this phantasmagoric society, so brilliant when viewed from outside but built on poverty and debt and emptiness. Thus *The Spendthrifts* is both an allegory of the ruling classes of Spain and a sermon on the classic Spanish theme, made familiar to us in *Don Quixote*, of illusion and reality. It is also a very brilliant, well designed and amusing novel.

GERALD BRENAN

I

It was a—how shall I describe it?—a fine sepulchral design in a highly audacious architectural style, grandiose in plan and rich in ornament. Some parts of it were severe and rectilinear, others Gothic and irregular with certain Plateresque tendencies where you would least expect them; finally there was a good deal of fretwork in the Tyrolean style that prevails in kiosks. It had pyramidal ramps and Graeco-Roman foundations, and broke out here and there into flying buttresses and parapets, pinnacles, gargoyles and cupolas. Moreover it was completely surrounded, top and bottom, left and right, by large quantities of torches, urns, vases, owls, wreaths of everlastings, hour glasses, scythes, palm leaves, broken columns and other emblems of Death and Eternal Life; all so crowded together that they seemed to be disputing inch by inch the sites they were to occupy.

In the middle of the mausoleum was a large plump angel leaning on a tomb in an afflicted manner and covering his eyes with his hand, as if unwilling to be seen weeping; his shamefaced attitude suggesting that he was of the masculine sex. This personage had a wing and a half of very fine curling feathers trailing softly down his back, and his women's feet were shod with little boots or sandals or sandshoes—for there was something of everything in this elegant interpretation of angelical footwear. On his head was a sort of garland of ribbons, which flowed on down to wrap themselves around his right arm. If at first glance it appeared that this being was groaning under his burdens—all those wings, flowers, ribbons and feathers, not to mention

13

an hour glass—a second look revealed that the real motive of his grief was the sad memory of the virginal creatures buried in the sarcophagus. Their names were displayed upon it in melancholy lettering, from whose lower extremities drops were falling, suggesting that tears were escaping from the marble itself. In this expressive way the grieving letters were made to contribute to the melancholy effect of the monument.

But the best thing of all, perhaps, was the willow: it was a weeping willow, one of those sentimental trees, which have had a more or less criminal part in every elegy committed since Rhetoric came into the world. Its undulating trunk rose up beside the sarcophagus, and from its high spreading branches fell a rain of leaves, so delicate, faint and suffering in appearance that they inspired a wish to give them smelling salts and bring them out of their poetic syncope. Such a willow was indispensible in an age in which the trees of romanticism had not yet been turned into firewood. The ground beneath it was sown with lovely plants and flowers on stalks of varying heights. There were daisies, pansies, passion flowers, sunflowers and enormous tulips, all respectfully bending down to show their grief.

The sense of distance or perspective had been obtained by showing a procession of other willows of gradually decreasing size, weeping their way towards the horizon. Behind these were soft outlines of mountains, wavering and collapsing as if they had been drinking, a little sea, a bit of river, and the confused profile of a city with castellations and Gothic towers. Above, in the space devoted to sky, was a round seal which seemed to be meant for the moon, judging by the white reflections which enamelled the waters and mountains.

The colours used in this beautiful work of art were brown, black and yellow, the gradations from dark shades to light serving to produce illusions of perspective. It was framed in an oval frame, perhaps eighteen inches in its greatest diameter, and seemed to be not so much painted, as drawn or printed. Was it a mezzotint, an etching, a steel engraving, a woodcut, or the incredibly patient work of a hard pencil, or of a pen dipped in Indian ink? For observe the excessive amount of detail. The leaves of the willow can be counted one by one, the foliage having been made by putting them on one after another, some so small that they can only be seen through a miscroscope. The chiaroscuro of the sepulchre has been secured by minute variations in the arrangement of lines—shadings and cross-hatchings that grow thinner or thicker according to the intensity of the values; while in the figure of the angel there are tints so delicate that they are only a mist of tiny dots, as if fine sand had fallen on a white ground. These dots, imitating the style of *taille-douce*, grow thicker in the shadows and thinner until they finally disappear in the lights, thus giving an illusion of relief.

This cenotaph was, in fact, a hair picture, a form of art which once had a certain vogue. And the artist, Don Francisco Bringas, displayed in it a truly extraordinary ability, a steadiness of hand and sharpness of eye which approached the marvellous—if they did not go a little beyond it.

II

This remarkable work was a delicate attention on the part of the good Bringas to his worthy friend, Don Manuel Maria José del Pez—an attempt to repay numerous debts of gratitude. For this busy member of the administration had given the Bringas family new proofs of his generosity in that year of 1868. Without even waiting for young Paquito to pass his Law examinations, he had got him a place in the Treasury with a salary of five thousand reals—not a bad beginning to a bureaucratic career at the age of sixteen. And the best part of it was that the boy who already had plenty to do, what with his classes at the University and his beloved lectures on the Philosophy of History and Common Law, didn't even have to put a foot inside the office except at the end of the month, when they made him a present of four hundred and sixteen reals and a few odd pennies for the sake of his handsome face.

In the self-satisfied mind of Rosalía Bringas the idea was firmly encrusted that this appointment was not a favour at all, but only the fulfillment of a duty that the State owed to precocious Spaniards. Still she was grateful for the promptness with which Pez had recognized and carried out the obligations of the Fatherland. The gratitude of Don Francisco was much more fervent and could not find sufficient means of expressing itself, since a present that would be at all commensurable with the favour received would not lie within the narrow resources of the family. It would have to be something that was original, striking and valuable, and yet did not cost anything; something that would spring from the fecund

16

imagination of Bringas himself and take on body and life in his creating artist's hands. Providence—which attends to everything—gratified our friend's noble desires.

A year or so before this time Pez's eldest daughter, an attractive child of fifteen, had been carried off to a better world. The disconsolate mother had kept her Juanita's hair, and was looking about for someone who could make a commemorative ornament from it; the sort of thing only to be found now, faded and dirty, in the windows of old-fashioned hair dressers or in the niches of cemeteries.

What the Señora de Pez wanted, one might say, was the putting into verse of a poetic thing that was in prose. She did not feel that the thick, fragrant tresses, in which it seemed that part of the soul of the poor child was still hiding, were sufficiently eloquent of themselves. What she wanted was something that was pretty; something that would speak the language spoken by light verse, tinkling glass ornaments, artificial flowers, and easy *Nocturnes* for the piano. As soon as he heard of this wish of Carolina's, Bringas cried Eureka with all the force of his spirit. He would be the versifier!

"I, Señora" he said eagerly, "I will do it."

"Ah, you can work in hair, can you? You are so clever—"

"What colour is the hair?"

"I will show it to you now" the mother said, opening, not without emotion, a small box which had once contained sweets and was now the blue and rose casket of funereal memories. "Just look at it—such a beautiful chestnut!"

"Oh yes, it's superb! But we will need some fair hair too."

"Fair hair? I have every colour. Look at these pale gold curls of my little Arthur who died when he was

17

only three. And then these of Joaquin's cut off when he was getting over scarlet fever. I could hardly bear to do it, but the doctor insisted."

"Splendid. We've got chestnut now and two shades of gold; but for the dark accents we need a little black."

"We can use Rosa's hair. Bring me some of your cuttings, daughter."

Don Francisco took the lock offered him with enthusiasm.

"You see, Carolina," he began, "I have an idea . . . It's as if I were seeing it. It's a cenotaph in a cemetery with willows and flowers . . . It is night . . ."

"Night?"

"I mean that to give an air of melancholy to the landscape everything should be rather dim. There will be water far off, a lake or a bay. Try to imagine it! The willows will spread their branches as if they were raining; between their leaves the disc of the moon will appear, its pale light silvering the peaks of the distant mountains, and making a rippling on the surface . . . The only trouble is that to get this beautiful effect I must have some white hair."

"Heavens, don't complain of a lack of white hair, when there's such a superfluity! I can supply you with all the rays of moonlight you need."

And she pulled out several long strands which Bringas added to the rest. How luckily it had turned out! He had two shades of fair hair, silver, ebony, and that romantic burnt sienna, which was to be the dominating note. He left the house in a state of feverish excitement, all impatience to start, and yet a little afraid to begin. His fancy was regaling itself in advance with a vision of the completed work, seeing that cenotaph and its weeping angel, the grieving willow and the distant landscape in all its watery and moonstruck melancholy.

Interrupting this beautiful vision of the unborn work, however, there sometimes flickered through the mind of the artist, like will o' the wisps, certain ideas about the possible expense he might be put to. And he encouraged these ideas, lending them the attention due to them from a highly practical man who, for some reason, was not exempt from spasmodic attacks of artistic creation. Counting to himself, he began to make a list of all the things he would need—.

III

"Gum: *two reals and a half*—it might come to *five reals*. Some florists' pincers—I think those I have are a little too big: *three reals*. A clear piece of glass: *a real and a half*. Four dozen pistils of saffron—that is, if I can't make them out of hair, but I'll try to first: *two and a half*. That comes to *fifteen reals*. Then there's the most expensive part, the convex glass and the frame. But I think I might be able to use the frame that's on Cousin Josefa's wool-work dog, if I regild it. Altogether, with the gilding, the convex glass, the cord, and any odds and ends I've forgotten, it might come to *twenty-eight* or *thirty reals*."

The following day happened to be a Sunday, and Bringas began his work. As he did not like any of the pictures of mausoleums that he had in his collection, he resolved to make up one of his own. But having no great confidence in his powers of invention, he composed the well-built edifice which has been described by putting together parts taken from various sources. The willow came from the *Tomb of Napoleon at St. Helena*, the weeping angel had been part of the monument to one of Fernando VII's wives in the Escorial, the landscape was taken from some Lamartinesque volume which was all pure syrup; while the flowers were gathered in an illustrated book on the *Language of Flowers* in the library of Doña Cándida.

This preparatory work on the design occupied the artist for three or four days, and he was so satisfied with the result when it was finished that he could not help calling in his wife to admire it, with a pretense of false modesty.

"Yes, it's really all so lifelike," Rosalía said, with appreciative enthusiasm. "You seem to be actually seeing the calm water; it's as if the moon were tickling it with light."

As soon as the design was completed, Bringas pegged it out on a board and put a glass of the same size over it, fixing the whole thing so that it could not move. This done, nothing else was needed but patience and neatness. He had to follow the lines of the design underneath the glass with hairs gummed on to the upper side—a really distracting task, given the difficulty of managing anything so intractable and slippery as human hair. The main outlines were not so hard to do; but in the shadows the artist had to cut hairs to the required lengths and stick them on with warmed glue, imitating the biting of the engraving tool on steel or wooden plates. In the finest tints of all, Bringas had subtilized his art until it had reached the microscopic. He was an innovator. No worker in this medium before him had ever attempted to make dots with hair, cutting it up with scissors until it was in such minute bodies that it resembled molecules, and then sticking these particles on one beside another, never quite touching, so that they resembled *taille douce*. For this work he used the very finest pincers or feathers brought to a point with saliva, picking up each piece separately and putting it in the required place which had previously been covered with varnish.

The use of different tones increased the maddening complexity of the work, since chestnut had to go here, black there, yellow somewhere else, gold in the angel's hair, silver in everything that lay under the direct rays of the moon. But the good man triumphed over all difficulties; he had the eyes of a lynx, and his fingers might have been the fingers of Zephyr, which caress flowers without stirring them. He could have made a

21

rosary of grains of sand, if he had set his mind on it, or carved Toledo Cathedral in a nutshell.

The whole month of March was employed on the cenotaph itself and on the willow beside it; the leaves kept budding one after another, and by the middle of April the angel had arms and a head. Everyone who saw the work was stiuck by its originality and beauty and gave Don Francisco a high place among the best artists of the time, declaring that if some foreigner could see his picture—for instance one of those rich Englishmen who come to Spain in search of rate objects—he would pay a large sum of money for it and carry it off to one of those countries where works of genius are properly appreciated.

Don Francisco's workshop was in the great embrasure of one of the windows looking out on the Campo de Moro. For the Bringas family lived in the Palace; in one of those apartments on the second floor which shelter the employees of the Royal Household. Enthralled by the hair picture, I have forgotten to say that at about this time, that is in February '68, Bringas was appointed a First Officer of the Privy Purse with a salary of thirty thousand reals, living quarters, medical attention, drugs, water, firewood and other perquisites which seem to be inherent in the vicinity of royalty. This appointment had realised the aspirations of his whole life, and he would not have exchanged his position—so exalted, so secure, so respectable!—for the throne of the Primate of Spain. The only thing that ever disturbed his perfect satisfaction were the rumours that were going round in that accursed year of '68, about the possibility of popular disturbances and the fear that the 'so-called revolution' might break out with violence. Although the suggestion that the Monarchy could come to an end sounded as absurd to our good man as the idea that the planets

might cease to revolve, nevertheless, when he happened to be present in some café or *tertulia* where he heard prognostications of rebellion, or announcements that *The Moment* had arrived, or lugubrious comments on the unpopularity of the Government or of the Queen, he shivered and felt his heart contract.

To reach his home on the second floor, Don Francisco had to climb no less than a hundred and twenty-four steps up the Ladies' Staircase from the patio. This Second Floor along with the Third make up a veritable city supported on the splendid ceilings of the Royal dwelling. There the aristocracy, middle classes and people mix peacefully together. It is a sort of royal republic, which the Monarchs wear as a crown; and linked together in its immense circuit it has diverse examples of every class of person.

The first time I ever went there I was accompanying Don Manuel Pez on a visit to Bringas in his new abode, and we began by losing ourselves completely in that labyrinth, where neither of us had ever been before. We had climbed the Ladies' Staircase to the Second Floor and been met there by a porter wearing a three cornered hat, who asked us our destination. When we told him, he pointed in the direction we should go and said:

"Turn left, then right, then go up a small staircase, then go down again ... Number 67."

IV

Easier said than done! We started off along a red tiled passage, which I could not help thinking of as a street or avenue because of its size; and from time to time as we walked we came to wide open spaces, which were so large that they could easily be described as Squares. These were flooded by sunlight coming in through big windows that opened on the patio. And this daylight, reflected from the white walls, penetrated a long way down the passages, gradually losing itself and growing fainter, until it died away altogether and red fans of gas appeared, each trembling in a smoky circle under its tin reflector.

As we went along we passed the doors of numerous apartments, some of them recently painted while others were discoloured and worn. Some of these doors had luxurious silken bell ropes, spoils filched from the Palace tapestry, while others had only frayed pieces of cord. But though they all had numbers on them, we could not find the number we were looking for. And we went on and on.

Sometimes we passed uninhabited apartments too, where the doors were hung with spider webs and the iron *rejas* were rusty. In some places we even passed through what seemed to be abandoned quarters of the town. We went up one staircase and later went down another and then I believe we went up a third. We were resolved to find our way unaided and would not ask assistance. Really we were enjoying the adventure of exploring these mysterious regions, and did not much mind losing our way. From time to time we came to one of the huge windows that opened on the terrace and tried to correct the errors of our course, using the cupola to fix our true position.

"There's no use coming here unless you have a chart and a compass" Pez said at last, on one of these occasions, beginning to get impatient. "This must be the South Wing—there's the Hall of Columns and the main staircase."

And in fact huge pyramidal forms covered with lead roofing showed us where they were.

Finally, after we had walked and walked, we came to a cul-de-sac, a large place lit by skylights, and had to retrace our steps. No one, looking at the straight classical lines of the Palace seen from outside, could possibly guess at the extraordinary irregularity of the city on its upper floors. The fact is that for a whole century they have been making alterations in the original plan of the building completely at hazard. They have been shutting up here and opening up there, condemning staircases and enlarging some apartments at the expense of others. There are dovecotes that once were drawing rooms and vestibules in which you can still trace the whitened ceiling of smaller rooms that have disappeared. In several places there are circular staircases which lead no one knows where, among sealed up doors and openings covered with wire, behind which there is only solitude, dust and shadows.

At one point Pez remarked:

"This must be one of the poor quarters."

We had come to a large open space lit by an enormous barred window where washing was hanging out on lines to dry, and the walls were scrawled over with drawings and indecent inscriptions. A number of women were washing clothes in large earthenware basins set in the passage, while others were sitting beside their doors combing their hair exactly as if they were sitting in the street.

"Have you lost your way?" one of the women enquired.

She had a boy baby in her arms wrapped in yellowish swaddling bands.

"We are looking for the apartments of Don Francisco Bringas," we told her.

"Bringas? Oh, yes, I know where he lives," said an old woman who was sitting near the window. "It's quite close. You mean the sacristan of the Chapel."

"No, no, señora, we are looking for one of the First Officials of the Privy Purse."

"Oh, then it will be downstairs on the terrace. Do you know your way to the fountain?"

"No."

"Or the Oratory? Or the dovecotes?"

But we did not know our way to a single place in that labyrinthine city. Nevertheless, we refused to admit ourselves vanquished and declined the offer of a small boy to be our guide.

"We are in the East Wing, that is the wing opposite to the one our friend lives in," Pez remarked, with the geographical emphasis of some character in Jules Verne. "We must set our course by the dome of the Chapel and try to get to the West Wing. But I swear I'll never come here again without a good map and provisions."

Before we started off on this second stage of our journey, we paused for a moment to look through the huge window at the beautiful view of the Plaza del Oriente and the part of Madrid which lies beyond it, in which we could count over fifty domes and steeples and bell towers. From that height Philip IV's horse looked like a toy and the Royal Theatre like a cottage. There were doves' nests below us, and we watched the doves precipitating themselves into the abyss of the Plaza in pairs or groups and then sweeping up again in curving lines at tremendous speed to light on the capitals and mouldings. Their cooing seems as much a part of the building as the stones of which it is made, for infinite numbers of them live in the innumerable niches of that artificial mountain and occupy it by hereditary right.

We went on again. Pez, as I say, seemed to be trying to put his geographical ideas into practice and kept saying:

"If we keep going to the right we must get to the West Wing, so we needn't be afraid to take this circular staircase down to the Second Floor—and now where are we? If we aren't back in the East Wing again! See the cupola over there on our right. The fountain must be somewhere on this side, look at the women coming and going with water jars . . . Oh, lord! I give up. Send me a guide, for heaven's sake. We must have walked at least five miles and I really can't take another step."

Just then Providence came to our aid in the not inconsiderable person of the widow of Garcia Grande, who suddenly appeared in front of us, emerging from one of the ugliest and shabbiest doors on the passage.

V

It is unnecessary to say how pleased we were at this encounter, while she, on the other hand, appeared to be disagreeably surprised by it, like some person who is trying to avoid being seen in some place which she feels to be unsuited to her rank. Her first remarks, confused and mixed up with the usual formulas of salutation, confirmed me in my impression.

"I won't ask you to come in, because I'm only up here temporarily while they are fixing up the apartment downstairs which the general's widow has vacated for me. These rooms are an atrocity, a calamity. But Her Majesty would insist on my coming to the Palace—I simply couldn't refuse her. It was always 'Candidita, I can't have you living so far away from me ... Candidita, come and live with me ... Candidita, choose any place you like that's empty upstairs.' Well it ended in my loading my furniture on six moving wagons and coming to the Palace. And then when I got here I found the rooms I was to have still full of masons. It's awful ... a wall has fallen down ... the plaster is in a terrible state ... the tiles go up and down under your feet like piano keys ... Well, the end of it was that I had to bring all my treasures up here to these rooms. It has all been most inconvenient ... Look at the two pictures by Rafael lying on the floor there, and the Tristan in that great bundle against the wall. My china is still in straw and my tables upside down and the screens and lamps and other little objects are all in complete disorder, still waiting to be arranged. It's atrocious, horrible ... You can imagine how nervous it makes me; I'm so accustomed to having my things nicely arranged, this lack of space depresses me. And then all this living among chambermaids and porters and pages and privy-emptiers exasperates me more than you can imagine. May Her Majesty forgive me for saying it, but she would have done better to leave me in my house in the Calle de la Cruzada. It was too large for me, I admit, and it was rather cold; but it was so convenient. There was room for everything . . . and all the carpets fitted. Here, I don't know . . . even when I'm in my own apartments it seems to me that I won't have room for all my things. But what can one do? *Laws propose and Kings dispose.*"

The last part of her speech was spoken in a tone of jovial resignation, the tone of one who is sacrificing her own tastes and comforts to the friendly caprice of a Queen. Meanwhile, as she talked, she was conducting us along the corridors and then out on to the terrace to take a short cut across it. There she pointed to a row of doors in an imposing manner, saying:

"That is where I am going to be. The Señora de Porta is moving along to make more room for me . . . I'm going to knock down a wall and put two rooms together, and open a door on the Caceres Staircase so that I can reach the principal gallery easily and get to the Ante-chamber. And I've told them to build three more chimneys and make a series of partitions."

Don Manuel, like the diplomat that he was, appeared to accept all these explanations; but actually he knew the speaker far too well to pay any heed to her grandiose pretensions. As for me, I had never even heard of the widow of Garcia Grande, so I listened to all this talk of knocking down walls and ordering alterations as if it were gospel. In my simplicity it sounded to me like the Royal language spoken just below the Throne, and respect sealed my lips.

We arrived at the Bringas' apartments at last, and then
we understood why we had passed them by before, for
the number was almost worn off. They were extremely
spacious and handsome, and the rooms, though few in
number, were so large that size made up for quantity.
Our friends' furniture looked absolutely lost in the huge
drawing room with its domed ceiling; but the portrait
of Rosalía's eminent ancestor, Don Juan de Pipaón,
which had been hung opposite the door, seemed to look
its contentment at every visitor who entered, as if saying:
"Here we really are in the right place!" while floods of
light and cheerfulness poured in through the windows
that opened on the Campo de Moro. There was no room
that could be spared as a study or workshop for Bringas,
so he had arranged a nook for himself in the room to
the right of the drawing room in the bay of one of the
huge windows, screening it off with a felt curtain. There
he had his work table and two or three chairs, while his
tools and all the odds and ends he used in his various
activities were hanging on a board on the wall. In a
similar window in another room, his son Paquito had
installed himself with his whole library as well as his
papers and class room notes, which already bid fair to
rival the archives of Simancas.

All the rooms were very large with arched ceilings; and
at the inner end of each was an alcove or closet of really
Cathedral-like proportions. These were unplastered but
whitewashed, their floors covered with thick matting,
and they were lighted by interior windows covered with
wire netting, which opened on to the great street-corridor
of the Palace-city.

The married pair had their bed in the alcove off the
room on the right of the drawing room, and as the one
off the drawing room itself was larger and better lit than
the others Rosalía used it as a dressing room and sewing

room, while the third alcove was turned into a dining room because it was near the kitchen. The children slept in two smaller interior rooms.

I don't know if it came from the fertile fancy of Bringas or the pedantry of Paquito, that idea of giving the rooms in their humble abode the names of the famous apartments underneath them. But before the family had been installed there a month all the Bringases, great and small, called the drawing room the Ambassadors' Room because it was used for the more ceremonial visits, while the room on the right of it, which contained the study of Bringas and the matrimonial bedroom was called *Gasperini*, probably because it was the most attractive of all. The other large room was given the name of the *Saleta*, while the dressing room received the nickname of the *Camón* from a hall in the Palace which was used as a guardroom. Even the little inside room where they did the ironing was called the *Furriela*, after the Quartermaster's Stores.

Don Francisco did not have to go out into the street at all to reach his office. He could either go down the Caceres Staircase and cross the patio, or, if the weather was bad, he could cross the high city to the Ladies' Staircase and then walk along under the arcades to the offices of the Privy Purse. As he seldom went out into the streets, even an umbrella had ceased to be necessary to him.

Living in the apartments around them there were some families which Rosalía, in spite of all her pride was obliged to admit as her superiors, while others were much below her conception of her position as a descendant of the Pipaóns. But she entered into friendly relations with all of them and returned all the ceremonial visits paid them when they first took up their residence in the city over the palace.

There was Doña Cándida . . .

VI

But before I go on with my story, I want to remove my disturbing presence out of it, and I can do this in a very few words by explaining the object of my visit to Señor de Bringas. I had sold some firewood and some hay by auction in Riofrio, and there was some difficulty about the price, which led to a dispute with a minor official of the Privy Purse, so that I found myself in danger of a lawsuit. I could almost feel the heavy hand of the Public-Prosecutor on my shoulder when I decided to try to kill the trouble at its source. Don Manuel Pez, the diplomatic adjuster of difficulties, the eternal recommender, the arranger of compromises, declared that he could get me out of my difficulty. I owed him various favours, but he owed me even more and greater ones, and he wanted to raise my gratitude to the level of his by himself taking me to see one of the first officials of the Privy Purse, since that would be the most effective means of recommendation. Everything turned out according to our wishes, and within two days of our visit my affair had been completely settled. On the fourth of October, Don Francisco's Saint's Day, I sent him two Bayonne capons and a dozen bottles of wine from my own vineyards, and I still did not think that I had done enough to show my appreciation of the service he had rendered me.

And now let us return to Doña Cándida. What a woman! She was always saying: 'I *must* go. My administrator is coming to see me and I mustn't keep him waiting, he is such an excessively busy man.' Or it would be: 'The rents of my houses haven't been paid on time lately.' Maximus Manso used to begin telling stories about her and then simply be unable to stop. In 1868 this lady still retained a good deal of her former imposing presence and of the grand manners she had acquired during her social reign in the five years when O'Donnell was in power. But she was rapidly using up the remains of what her husband had left her, and there was not a day on which some bit of jewelry or small picture or piece of furniture did not leave the house with the object of bringing in money for current expenses. If I had more space I would describe her battles with her landlord during the time when she owed him six months rent. The Queen finally saved her from these difficulties by paying the money herself and offering Doña Cándida one of the apartments on the top floor of the Palace, which the poor woman did not hesitate to accept.

"I've only moved into this attic to please Her Majesty, so that I can be near her while they are altering the rooms on the terrace for me. But what a dilatory man that architect is! I'm going to give him a piece of my mind soon."

This was always her story. But the months went by and still the widow did not leave her temporary quarters. At the time when Pez and I ran into her, the famous pictures by Rafael and the large picture by Tristan had been mouldering and gathering dust for over a year, along with all the other precious objects which by some miracle had never found their way into museums.

Doña Cándida was one of the Bringas family's most constant visitors. Rosalía felt a sort of respectful affection towards her, and always listened to her submissively, conceiving her to be a great authority on social matters and on the proprieties in general. In the eyes of the Señora de Bringas, Cándida's brilliant past, though somewhat worn by time, had left rays of prestige and nobility around her Roman bust and presumptuous manners. This aureole fascinated Rosalía, who only increased her respectful behaviour towards majesties after they had fallen, and she always appeared to take quite seriously all that talk of *my administrator*, and *my houses*. In any case Cándida talked so much and so completely at random on all occasions and expressed herself with such conviction and such absolute certainty of being right, that it would have been quite impossible to argue with her on any subject.

Her rooms were in the East Wing, the poorest part of what we have agreed to call the city, but no one else who lived there paid so many visits or spent so little time at home. Her whole day went by in going from one apart-ment to another and traversing every part of the colossus, from the kitchens to the dovecotes. At night she would return to her 'temporary lodgings', as tired as if she had been all over Madrid, without ever having been out into the streets at all. At this time she had no family except a niece of nine or ten called Irene, the orphaned child of one of Garcia Grande's brothers, who had been a gentle-man in waiting to Her Majesty. This little girl was the bosom friend of Bringas' small daughter, and the two of them could be seen every afternoon with their dolls in one hand and something to eat in the other, playing on the terrace or in the brighter parts of those long covered streets.

The person of highest rank who lived in the city, one who in Rosalía's eyes occupied a place immediately below the Royal Family, was the widow of General Minio, who had been chief Gentleman in waiting to Her Majesty. All her neighbours called her by the affectionate nickname of Doña Tula except Rosalía who never spared her title. It was all 'Condesa this' and 'Condesa that' with her. This noble and kindhearted lady was a sister of the Marquesa de Telleria and of Alexander Sanchez Botin, a deputy who had in his time been a member of half a dozen different parties. The Sanchez Botins are an old family, deriving, I believe, from some manor house among the oaks of Bierzo, and being remotely related to the Aransis family.

The two sisters were married on the same day; Milagros to the Marques de Tellería and Gertrudis, the elder, to Colonel Minio, who rapidly rose to be a general by winning courtiers' battles in the Palace antechamber. Not a Royal Birthday passed without his receiving a Cross or being advanced a grade in rank; and when he could rise no higher in his profession they made him the Conde de Santa Barbara, a title taken from a property he had in Navarre. And the name has a certain suggestion of gunpowder, which went well with his vocation, although it was said of him that he had never smelled any powder except what is wasted in salutes. The reputation for valour which he enjoyed was probably only founded on the fact that he was extremely stupid; for our ideas are in such a state of confusion that we find it easier to turn people into heroes if they can hardly write their names. What is certain is that Don Pedro Minio was an imposing figure at a parade or taking the salute at some barracks inspection or leading the cheers at some military review; but except for being mentioned as present at one as two unimportant skirmishes in the first Civil War, the military history of our country has nothing to say of him. He will go down to posterity however as the author of those celebrated remarks about the *Sword of Demosthenes* and the *Cloth of Pentecost* and by his suggestion about 'going to Havana by way of the Philippines'. These sayings of his were diligently collected by his subordinates and form a diverting collection of absurdities. The Queen knew them all by heart and used to tell them very amusingly. But let us not waste any more time in disturbing the ashes of this Nobody, of whom his widow used to say in the most secret depths of intimacy that he was an ox with decorations, and talk of her instead.

Doña Tula was so unlike the Marquesa de Tellería that it hardly seemed possible that they could be children of the same parents, and she was equally unlike her brother. The rare gifts with which she was adorned came from quite another sort of human distinction—from misfortune, the privilege of those beings who are advancing towards perfection. Her two sons had inherited along with the general's name his stupidity and crudeness, and were both complete ne'er-do-wells. It would be impossible to tell what their unfortunate mother suffered while she was trying to get them through their schooling and into the cavalry; she passed five or six years of continual struggle against the stupidity and laziness of the boys and their difficulties with their reluctant teachers. Thanks to the name they bore and to the letters which the Queen wrote whenever it became necessary, they were finally graduated, became officers and were gazetted. And then a new series of difficulties began, to embitter Doña Tula's existence. Quarrels, duels, drunken bouts, summonses, reckless gambling, unpaid debts were everyday occurrences. And their mother had to smooth everything over by using her influence or by paying out money. It came to such a point at last that when the elder, who was called Pedro Minio like his father, determined to go off to Cuba, she had no energy left to oppose him. The other son was set on marrying a woman of bad character, and this was another contest for the mother. It was after this that she made her famous remark. They were speaking of children, and of the mothers who want them, and the mothers who have too many.

"Oh, children—" Doña Tula said, with the saddest of accents. "They are a nine months illness and a convalescence that lasts all your life."

While Doña Tula's children were stupid and ugly and perfect demons to boot, her sister Milagros seemed to have given birth to four angels, all beautiful, charming and clever—that little Leopold, so naughty and delightful, Gustavito so precocious and sensible, and Luisito, such a mystic that he seemed to be a saint's apprentice. And, best of all, Maria, of the green eyes and Helenic profile, a Venus excavated from the ruins of Greece, a living sculpture by a master hand. What mother would not have been enchanted to possess such children? Doña Tula adored her nieces and nephews as if they were her own children—and children, moreover who had caused her no pain, hers only for the pleasures of life. Maria, then about fifteen, was her favourite, and the beautiful child passed more than half her time with her aunt, while on feast days a number of her little playmates came to spend the day in the Condesa's apartments too.

And what a sight the terrace was then! There were nymphs in short dresses, which were soon going to descend to the ground, and nymphs in long dresses which had been short only a fortnight before. Those who had received this investiture as women went about in groups arm in arm, trying to behave correctly and talk discreetly, while the smallest ran about showing half a leg. Then, when some youthful admirer of one of the girls, with a stick and coloured cravat and light coloured overcoat, sometimes even smoking a cigarette in an amber holder, found his way to one of the galleries—ah, who could describe all the laughter and hiding that went on then, the awkwardnesses and innocent games, the delightful foolishness of those fresh creatures just opening their coroilas to the sun of life!

This playful band of women-in-the-making often invaded the Bringas' dwelling. Rosalía, who was delighted to come into relations with Doña Tula and the Tellerías received them with open arms and regaled them with sweets which she had brought from the Palade confectioners for the purpose. And Don Francisco seemed to be enchanted too:

"Play, shout, make as much noise as you please; it doesn't bother me!" he would say to them gaily from the depths of his window, where he would be sitting submerged in his sea of hair.

And the children did not need to be told twice. They took him so much at his word that they would run dancing from *Gasperini* to the *Saleta* and then go in leaps and bounds from the *Camón* to *Furriela*. But however much Don Francisco expressed his pleasure at seeing his apartments full of seraphim, he often found them a perfect nuisance, especially when they took it into their heads to admire the hair picture and crowded round his table so closely that he could hardly breathe. Then he would say to them:

"Children, for heaven's sake go a little further back. You can see without suffocating me or turning over the varnish ... Take care, Maria, your breath is blowing away those white hairs ... Further back, please, I beg you ..."

VII

The events which I am recounting took place as I have said in the spring of '68; and the Holy Thursday of that year was one of the days on which the children were liveliest and made most noise. Don Francisco, sanctifier of religious festivals, was present at the ceremony in the Chapel, in full dress with his Cross and everything, and Rosalía went down to the Royal Apartments too, convinced that her presence was indispensable if the ceremonies were to go off with the proper éclat and brilliance. Cándida, however, did not go down; she said that she was tired of ceremonies; but really it was because she did not have anything to wear.

The little girls invaded Doña Tula's apartments at a very early hour that morning; but the Condesa had to go downstairs because of her position at Court, so she went off magnificently dressed, leaving them in the care of a lady who lived with her. And how the children enjoyed themselves that day! And how they tormented their youthful admirers, treacherously inviting them to climb up to one of the dovecotes from which they declared that they would get a good view, and then locking them up and leaving them there until midday.

As the girls were friends of the Sacristan, who was a neighbour of Cándida's, they were allowed to sit on the steps leading down to the Chapel and had a view through the half opened doors of the Patriarch's mitre, two snuffed-out candles in the large candelabrum, an altar covered with purple cloth and the bald heads of some of the chaplains, as well as a glimpse of various masculine breasts loaded with Crosses and Ribbons—but

41

that was all. Later on however they managed to see a good deal of the handsome ceremony of feeding the poor which takes place after the ceremonial washing.

In the South Wing of the terrace there are some large glassed-in openings protected by wire netting, which give light to the principal staircase, the guardroom and the Hall of Columns. Looking out through them you see the ceilings so close to you that the figures which decorate them are monstrous and the painting looks very coarse. Huge angels and nymphs stretch their enormous legs out towards Scotland, riding on clouds which look like bales of gray cotton. Other figures seem to be lifting the framework of the ceiling into the air with the force of their colossal muscles; while the flowers of the carpet far below look like flowers painted in a miniature.

A great many people of every sort and class had arrived early to get places near the windows that look down on the Hall of Columns, because from there it was possible to see the dinner given to the poor. The women crowded as close as they could to the great circles of glass, and those who could get to the front row, even if they had to elbow their way there, could enjoy the sight of the pompous act of Royal humility and interpret it as they pleased. There was a good deal of noise and confusion, while some of those from outside who had been invited in tried to get the best peep-holes for themselves. But Cándida put on the air of authority which she knew how to assume on important occasions and ordered them to leave one of the windows free for the sole use of the Tellería and Lantigua and Bringas children. She really was the devil and got her way in the end by threatening to have everyone turned out at once if they didn't obey her.

Seen like that from the roof, the spectacle in the Hall of Columns was an exceedingly curious one. The table

at which the twelve poor old men were sitting was hardly
visible; but the table for the twelve old women was just
opposite the windows in the ceiling and everything that
happened at it could be clearly seen. And how embarrassed
the poor things looked in their new woollen dresses and
shawls and new head handkerchiefs, shocked to find
themselves in such a scene of pomp, served by the Queen
herself—they who only the day before had been begging
a sad penny outside some Church door. They never
lifted their eyes from their plates except to stare with
alarm at the personages who served them. Some of them
even shed tears, more of distress than of gratitude—for
their situation among the powerful of the earth as reci-
pients of this formal charity was one more calculated to
humiliate them than to make them proud. Just as all the
forces of the imagination would be baffled by the task
of representing Christ in a frock coat, so this palace
comedy seemed to have little if anything to do with the
teachings of the New Testament.

Trays of food were brought to the door by men servants
and handed to the distinguished persons who acted as
waiters on this pious occasion. These ladies and gentlemen
formed a chain and passed the trays along until they
reached the hands of the King and Queen, who presented
the food to the poor people with a certain air of benevol-
ence and courtesy, which was the only sympathetic note
in their theatrical farce. But the unfortunate creatures at
the table did not eat; they were much too frightened.
Their trembling hands could hardly have found the way
to their mouths. So after the food had been placed before
them, other men servants went about collecting it again
and packing it into the baskets which were placed behind
each poor person's chair. Shortly afterwards, when the
Royalties and nobles had left the Hall, the old men and
women went out too carrying their baskets. And near

the Palace Confectionery various Madrid inn-keepers and other people in the catering trade were waiting to buy the food they had been given for a few duros.

While the scene around the tables was going on, the cluster of charming little spectators never ceased their voluble chatter. Maria kept wishing that she could be down there too passing trays with the others, dressed in a beautiful dress with a long train. One of the Lantigua girls was actually bold enough to suggest that the whole thing really resembled a badly acted farce, while her sister was entirely taken up with the gorgeous dresses and uniforms.

"Look, look, there's Mama! Can you see her there in the peach coloured dress? She's standing by Señor de Pez, talking to him."

"Yes, they're looking up. She knows we are here. And I can see Don Francisco too, just there by the Chamberlain of the week. And there's Mother beside him!"

"How handsome the Marquesa looks in her mauve skirt and shawl! And there's Doña Tula! Doña Tula, Doña Tula . . . She's looking up, she sees us . . . Here we are . . ."

"These ceremonies are a terrible worry to my aunt," Maria said. "You can't think how many letters of recommendation she gets beforehand. For twenty-four places there are always at least three hundred recommendations. Every day there are letters and messages from this Marquesa and that Condesa. You'd think that they were going to be given some high post."

"You don't have to tell me about it!" said Cándida in a tone of disgust. "Yesterday and today I haven't had a moment to call my own. Tomasa, the chambermaid, who is a neighbour of mine, was in charge of washing the twelve poor women and changing their dirty rags for the clean clothes they are wearing today. Poor things! It was the second time that water had touched them in their lives; and it would have been the first if they hadn't

been baptized. But what a scene it was this morning! I
believe they used up a demijohn of eau de cologne. I
tried to help a little with it, because it seemed to me
that I was doing something towards obeying the com-
mands of our Lord Jesus Christ. And I really believe that
if I hadn't been there they would never have finished at
all this morning. But, speaking frankly, if I were a poor
person and they brought me here to go through this
ceremony, I wouldn't see anything to be grateful about—
because really what they receive isn't nearly enough to
compensate them for the fright they suffer and the dis-
agreeableness of all that washing."

But the children around her were still at a romantic
age and could not understand the more practical point
of view of the experienced Doña Cándida. They found
it all well done and beautiful, in keeping with the double
majesty of Church and Throne.

Isabelita Bringas was a weak, rickety, clever child, and
showed signs of a tendency towards epilepsy. Her sleep
was often disturbed by terrible nightmares which were
followed by vomiting and convulsions, and sometimes,
when these symptoms did not appear, the disease showed
itself in an even more alarming form. She would become
dull and numb, and seem to have difficulty in understanding what was said to her, losing for the time being
all her childish vivacity. It was impossible to scold her
for it, and her schoolmistress had been warned not to
punish her or try to force her attention at such times. If
she had seen anything exciting during the day or heard
any painful story, it would all appear again that night in
her troubled sleep. And this was aggravated by any
indiscretion in eating, for then the work of digestion
became too much for the poor child's slight strength.

That Holy Thursday Doña Tula gave her little friends
a splendid repast, and Isabelita ate a great deal and

enjoyed it extremely. But the poor child had not been in bed long before she began to be feverish and delirious. The people and objects which she had been seeing during that happy, exciting day kept coming back to her, but mixed up with all sorts of nonsensical incidents. She played the games on the terrace over again; but the children were all terribly changed and Cándida looked like a great black shepherdess guarding the flock. Then she was sitting at the hole in the high window looking down at the ceremony of feeding the poor; but the figures on the ceiling came to life and threatened the spectators, thrusting out their fists at them. Suddenly the Royal March began to play—was the Queen coming up on the terrace? No. Through the doors that opened on the Ladies' Staircase her own Mama appeared, leaning on the arm of the Señor de Pez, while her Papa gave his arm to the Marquesa de Tellería. How splendidly her Mama and the Marquesa advanced, drawing those trains after them that seemed miles in length! And how strong and well built the two men looked! They were coming up to Doña Tula's apartments to have some refreshments. And later on they were going with the Court and *La Señora* to visit the holy relics. Then all the doors in the upper part of the Palace began opening, and different uniforms appeared in each of them, blue cloth and red cloth, gold and silver braid, an infinity of three cornered hats.

As her delirium increased the child saw the city shining in many colours. Why, it was a doll's city! And what dolls! White wigs were appearing everywhere, and the doors kept opening on the Second Floor passages and letting out those handsome figures of wax and stuffed cloth and porcelain, while on the staircase gold lace coming up was passing gold lace going down ... And all of them were hurrying and they all kept repeating *The Hour has come!* Then they rushed away down the principal staircase.

In the courtyard below the halberdiers were going round and round with the coachmen and lackeys: it was like a great casserole in which many-coloured human limbs were turning round and round in the heat. Her Mama and Papa appeared, and how handsome they looked! But Papa would be even finer when they made him a Knight of the Holy Sepulchre. The King had promised to arrange it, and was going to provide the uniform and all the accessories too, the sword and spurs and everything. How handsome her Papa would be with his white coat, with everything white! . . . At this point the poor child felt her whole being wrapped up in this idea of whiteness, and at the same time felt a horrible fullness and obstruction, as if all the scenes and objects her mind was producing were contained inside her small stomach. With agonized convulsions she threw it all out; and the delirium decreased and she felt an immense relief. Her mother had sprung from her bed to come to her assistance; and Isabelita, now wide awake, could hear the affectionate voice saying:

"It's all over now, darling. It was nothing."

VIII

The beauty of the Marquesa de Tellería was still striking, though she had already passed the meridian of life;
and the unusually skilful methods of restoration which
she employed did not yet betray themselves as those
plasterings and paintings which are useless because of the
bad condition of the building to which they are applied.
And she had strong defences against time—in her clever-
ness, her elegance, and her talent for dress; as well as in
the sympathy which she could inspire in those who did
not know her too well.

Rosalía Bringas was fascinated by all these qualities,
but particularly by the Marquesa's exquisite taste in dress
materials and styles. Indeed she held the authority of
Milagros in such estimation that her own opinions on
these subjects were simply reflections of the august
truths her friend proclaimed. What she said made up a
Code of Laws to be invoked on any subsequent occasion.
And as Milagros not only legislated, but illustrated her
doctrine by good example, dressing in a manner quite
beyond criticism, the Señora de Bringas, who had developed a perfect passion for dress, elevated an alter to her
in her soul.

The widow of Garcia Grande fascinated Rosalía too,
but in another way: by her prestige as an historical figure.
Rosalía respected her as one might respect the goddess
of a dead religion. But Milagros was the representative
of a living dogma and of gods still in power; and no one
in the world, not even Bringas, had such influence over
the descendant of the Pipaóns. She, who could be
dominating and somewhat discourteous to equals and

inferiors, became almost timid in the presence of her idol and mistress.

It was the presents which her rich cousin Augustin Caballero had given her, and then his handing over to her of all the handsome things he had bought for his bride-to-be (before he discovered that incident in her past and the marriage was broken off) that had first awakend this passion for clothes in Rosalía. Her former modesty in regard to dress, always more a necessity than a virtue, had been submitted to a proof from which it did not emerge victorious. In earlier days her husband's economical habits had put a brake on her appetite for luxury, and as long as Rosalía had never tasted the fruit forbidden by the household god everything went well. But the apple once eaten, farewell simplicity! After having had so many handsome new dresses to wear, how could Rosalía resign herself to making over old clothes and never being in style again?

As Bringas disapproved of his wife's spending money on new clothes or ornaments, she pretended to take no interest in the styles; but behind closed doors she was always altering her dresses and interpreting fashion plates more or less freely. If Milagros came to see her when Bringas was at the office, they could talk at their ease and give rein to the passion that dominated them. But if the good man was in his window submerged in his hair picture, they would shut themselves up in the *Camón*. There Rosalía would pull the drawers out, softly so as not to make any noise, and take out skirts, bodices which needed remaking and materials either cut out or still in the piece, and spread them all out on the sofa, the chairs, the chests, or the floor if necessary. And then there would begin a feverish consultation on what could be done with the means at their disposal, so as to get the most striking effect within the limits of good taste. These

51

consultations were endless, and if they could have been taken down would have formed a curious encyclopaedic report on this feminine passion, which has certainly done more to ruin the world than all the revolutions put together. The two women always talked in low voices so that Bringas should not hear them; and there was a continual rapid low vehement murmuring, sometimes suggesting indecision and anxiety, sometimes enthusiasm over a happy idea. The French expressions which they used stood out from the texture of our language rather oddly, but I must put them in, even if I have to stick them down with pins, so as not to lose the exotic flavour of the classic language of dressmaking.

Rosalía would say, looking at some design:

"To tell the truth, I don't understand this picture at all. I can't see how you can bring the skirts of this Guards' *casaque* together at the back."

"Let's not bother about the patterns," Milagros would say, "If you follow them too closely it's apt to look affected. Anyway you must decide on the material first. Are you going to get the white muslin with the foulard spots?"

"No. I've decided on the *gros de Naples* in ashes of roses. Sobrino said he would let me have it at twenty-four reals."

"Good. Well, if you've really fixed on that, I'd have the skirt made with four frills about four inches wide— No, I think I'd have five or six. And I'd edge them with a narrow bias of pale green *gros*. Do you see what I mean?"

Rosalía would contemplate this abstract creation with a sort of ecstasy.

"Oh yes, perfect . . . And the bodice?"

Milagros, picking up a half-made bodice, would model the cloth into lapels and coat tails with her clever fingers as she talked.

"The Guards' *casaque* will be open in front, with lapels faced with the same green *gros* as the edgings and the skirts of the coat will be turned back ... like this ... to show the green lining and will fasten at the back with studs ..."

Here she put her hands behind her and pleated her own dress over that prominent part of the person where the skirts of the coat were to come together.

"You understand what I mean? It will be perfectly charming, I think. Remember you'll need a pleated battiste *guimpe* trimmed with *valenciennes* to wear with it—and the sleeves ought to be very long and full so that they fall over the hands."

"Oh, it will be wonderful! I think I might have a *guimpe* that would do ..."

"I saw the one that Pilar San Salamo brought back from Paris to wear with her dress for the theatre." Here Milagros would speak with real aesthetic emotion. "Such a dress! The most heavenly thing I ever saw in my life!"

"What is it like?" Rosalía would enquire with intense interest.

"It's a heavy rose-coloured silk and the skirt trails on the ground and is finished with a flounce covered with embroidery—you never saw anything so *chic*. There are eight bands of black velvet on it ..."

"And fringe?"

"Yes, four rows of gold fringe. Then there's a short jacket gathered into a belt, and the material goes on to form a great *pouf* ... Do you see what I mean? ... It's *so* original. Then there's a long train which begins under the bustle and is trimmed with gold fringe too, with a great rose-coloured bow over the fringe. The whole effect is marvellous!"

"How is the bodice made?"

"Cut very low. And the *guimpe* is the very latest thing ... silk gathered in with black velvet ribbons running through eyelet embroidery ..."

53

But here Rosalía would interrupt suddenly, snatching everything up in alarm:

"I think I hear Bringas coming—all this concealment is a torture."

And Milagros would help her to push everything back into the drawers again, saying as they did so:

"Yes, I hear his cough. My dear, your husband might be the Customs, he's so sharp after silks. We must hide our contraband."

These hours which Rosalía spent with the Marquesa discussing the best way to make her dresses with the means available were extremely happy ones; but an even greater pleasure for her was going round the shops with her friend, though she passed unhappy moments because she could not buy the beautiful things she saw in them. Time went by unnoticed, while Milagros made the clerks show her everything in the shop. She passed from sudden enthusiasms to cold disdain, always tried to bargain and in the end generally bought a number of articles and had them put down to her account. Rosalía, on the other hand, turned her money over a great many times before she bought anything at all, and always paid on the spot; and her purchases were seldom anything more than remnants, or pieces of some antiquated material which she thought she could use to renovate her dresses.

But one day in *Sobrino Hermanos* she saw a mantle.— What a garment it was! The passion of the collector in the presence of a rare piece, the enthusiasm of the hunter who sees a splendid beast before him, give but a slight idea of this formidable passion for dress that some women have. Rosalía could not take her eyes off the superb creation, as the patient shop assistant showed it to them along with numerous others and then piled them up on the counter as if they were empty sacks. She asked the

price hesitantly and could not bring herself to try to bargain over it. She was as much alarmed by the enormous amount they asked as seduced by the splendour of the garment, in which velvet, broadcloth and brilliant silk cording were wonderfully combined.

Even after she had gone home she could not get the mantle out of her mind. All that day and all that night she could think of nothing else; and her blood was so heated by the ardour of her desire that she was almost afraid that she might have an attack of erysipelas if she did not gratify it.

The next day she went shopping with Milagros again, but with the fixed intention of not going near Sobrino's where the great temptation was. However the Devil so arranged it that they went there after all. And once more the counter was covered with white boxes—those chests made of satin-finished pasteboard in which the dreams of ladies are stored away. Once more the shop assistant took out the mantles one by one and laid them in a black pile, until at last the favourite appeared with its elegant form and its luxurious passementerie, in which black jet sequins trembling between fringes confirmed everything that the poets have said about the mantle of night. Rosalía actually felt a coldness in her chest and a burning in her temples as she looked at it, and the nerves in her shoulders suggested the sensation of contact so vividly that she imagined that she already had it on.

"Buy it, for heaven's sake," Milagros said to her, in such an insinuating tone that the shop assistants and Sobrino himself could do no less than applaud the suggestion. "Why should you deprive yourself of something that suits you so well?"

And when the shop people went off a little to attend to some other customers, the Marquesa whispered to her friend:

"Buy it, if you like it. Really it's not dear, considering . . . As you're with me they won't expect you to pay for it now, because I have an account here. They won't even send you the bill for several months, not till the beginning of summer probably, perhaps not till the end of the year."

The idea of this long reprieve made Rosalía hesitate and think more seriously of the purchase. The truth was that the seventeen hundred reals they asked for it was not an impossible sum for her; she could get it together quite easily if she gave the second-hand clothes dealer some things she no longer wanted, and if in addition to that she reduced the household expenses with a firm hand. The trouble was that Bringas would never permit such a large expenditure on something that was not absolutely necessary. Hitherto she had always made her cloaks and mantles herself, borrowing one from some friend for a model. By buying remnants in the sales at Santa Cruz's and putting pieces together and hiding the joinings, she had managed to obtain a satisfactory effect at small expense, though with much labour. But there was absolutely no comparison between her own poor creations and this brilliant model just arrived from Paris. And she knew that Bringas would never authorize such a luxury: it would seem to him positively *Asiatic*. She would have to deceive him in some way . . . No, no. She couldn't decide to do such a thing. It was too serious. Such an extravagance would be too violent a break with all the traditions of the family.—But the mantle was so beautiful. The Parisians seemed to have made it expressly for her. Should she buy it . . . Yes? . . . No?

IX

She bought it. And so explain her possession of such a superb garment, she had to call to her aid the story—already a little worn—of the Queen's munificence. Rosalía, it seemed, had happened to be in the antechamber one day when they were unwrapping some boxes of clothes which had just arrived from Paris. The Queen tried on a *canezou* which was a little too small for her and than a jacket which was too large, and the Royal modiste was making suggestions about alterations. A little later they opened another box—such a charming box lined with cretonne and covered with a material that looked like satinette. There were three mantles in it. One of them fitted Her Majesty to perfection; but the other two didn't suit her, and she said:

"Try this one on, Rosalía. What do you think of it? It might have been made for you."

And really it couldn't have fitted her better if it had been.

"How well it looks on you! Turn round, let me see. Do you know I really can't bear to let you take it off. Keep it on."

"But, Señora, for heaven's sake ..."

"No, keep it on. It's yours by the right of conquest! The truth is you've got such a figure!"

The Queen was accustomed to making presents to her friends in this gallant manner; and the good Bringas almost shed tears as he listened to the story. If I am not mistaken the swallowing of this large bolus took place in April when Rosalía had not even begun to worry about paying the bill. There seemed to be plenty of time, for she knew that she could get the money together in a couple of months. And then—out of the blue—the Bill! It was at the time of the Infanta Isabel's marriage, and Rosalía had been kept so busy with all the preparations for it that she had not even thought of the money she owed Sobrino, so that she was overcome with surprise and alarm when the bill collector arrived, and gazed at the paper he handed her absolutely unable to think of anything to say. For it was simply impossible to think of paying it. She had never been in such straits before, because it was a law with Bringas never to buy anything unless he actually had the money in hand. In the end she stammered something about coming around herself to pay the bill 'tomorrow, no, the day after, some day soon'.

Fortunately Bringas was out at the time. But Rosalía passed the next two or three days in a state of great anxiety; every time the door-bell rang she was afraid that it was the cursed man from the shop bringing his horrid paper again. The very thought that this might happen turned her alarm into real terror, and she went over every possible means she could think of for getting herself out of the scrape. Only a few days before she had actually had nearly half the sum she needed in the house, but she had spent it on things for the children. For she attached the same importance to her children's clothes as to her own, and wanted them always to be dressed so that they were fit to mingle with the children of the best families of the city. In these purchases—to wit, some collars, a hat for Isabelita, some blue stockings, some red gloves, a sailor's hat with *Numancia* in gold letters on the ribbon for Alfonsito—she had spent no less than seven hundred reals, which she had only got together by substituting for the customary dish of veal at dinner a dish of brains or a savoury omelette.

Her money-box only produced a hundred and twenty reals—What could she do, oh Lord, what could she do? She must get the money somehow. But where? How? She made discreet hints to Milagros; but the Marquesa seemed to be affected that day by a sort of intellectual deafness. This absence of mind might have been translated as 'My dear friend, knock at some other door.' But what door? At Cándida's? She made the attempt, and found that the illustrious widow would have been only too glad to help her; but most unfortunately, the rents of her houses had not been paid on time that quarter and her man of affairs hadn't brought the money yet. And then she had had to spend so much already on repairs . . . In short there was no salvation in that direction either.

In the end, however, Providence sent Rosalía the assistance she craved in the shape of Gonzales Torres, an old friend who visited them as frequently in the Palace as he had when they lived in the house in Castanilla. Torres handled other people's money for them, and often had considerable sums for disposal, out of which he somehow managed to make a profit during the brief time that they were in his possession. Taking advantage of her husband's absence one day when he called, Rosalía told Torres frankly all about her trouble; and the good man was able to set her mind at rest in a moment. How quickly the roses returned—to speak poetically—to the pale cheeks of the lady! Torres luckily happened to have just then a considerable sum to place belonging to Mompous y Brieul; and he could easily let Rosalía have what she wanted for a month. If she would promise to pay the seventeen hundred reals back at the end of thirty days, there wouldn't be the slightest difficulty about it; indeed he would be only too pleased to do it for her. A month! She wouldn't need a month to save the money in if she reduced the usual household expenses with implacable parsimony and also sold some of her clothes which were no longer in style. But one thing . . . absolute secrecy in front of Bringas.

When she was sure of being able to pay *Sobrino Hermanos*, a terrible weight fell from her conscience. Fear no longer made her breath come short when she thought of that fatal bill collector presenting himself while Bringas was at home. She recovered her appetite and her nerves grew quiet again. The truth is that for a few days she had been suffering from something so like a nervous breakdown that she had had difficulty in keeping her husband from calling in the doctor.

Torres brought the money that same afternoon; and Rosalía was putting on her cloak to go out and pay the bill at *Sobrino's* when Milagros came in. How handsome she looked and how elegant!

"I've brought the blue ribbons for the *canezou*," she said. "Look, it's the newest shade, shot with green. See what a difference it makes! Just let me rest for a moment, and then we can go out together; I came in my coach.— Oh, you must see the enchanting hats *Las Toscanas* have got in! There is one that is perfect, really divine, so original that it's almost supernatural. Try to imagine it . . . It's a *Florian* of Italian straw, trimmed with wild flowers and black velvet ribbon . . . Here, at this side, it has an aigrette with a black foot, caught like this . . . At the back there's a black veil that falls down to the shoulders. But they are asking an eye out of your head for it."

Rosalía positively felt a throbbing in her temples as she pictured to herself—with admirable powers of creating an hallucination—the wonderful hat which had been so well described.

"Even if we don't mean to buy anything we could just pass that way and look at it," she said.

They went out together and got into the coach which was waiting at the Prince's Gate, and Milagros chattered tirelessly as they drove. Her talk was all of the things she had been looking at, the stuffs for summer dresses which *Sobrino Hermanos* had just got in, and of the great works she was planning in the dressmaking line—as much, that is, as she could manage on the rather limited funds to which her husband had reduced her. Suddenly she remembered that she ought to collect a brooch which she was having repaired and made over at the jewellers. What a nuisance! She hadn't brought her pocket book; and the shop assistant wouldn't give her credit because she had once had a dispute with the owner over something or other. Oh, she needn't worry about that, Rosalía had plenty of money with her.

"Oh, good. I'll give it to you tomorrow, or the day after, anyway the next time I come to see you."

For a moment the wife of our good Bringas was rather disconcerted, and didn't know whether to regret the suggestion she had made or congratulate herself on the service which she had been able to offer her friend in such a gallant manner. But the human soul is a perpetual source of remedies for its own ills, and Rosalía soon cured herself with the following reasons, which occurred to her opportunely and ran something like this: "I'll pay half of *Sobrino's* bill and promise to pay the other half without fail next month; I'll give Milagros the thirty duros she needs, poor thing; and I'll still have enough left to get that piece of foulard, and two or three feathers for Isabelita's hat, and those mother-of-pearl buttons I need—I really can't do without any of those things."

And this plan was carried out to the letter, in conformity with the rationalisations made while hurrying about in the coach from shop to shop under the influence of an intoxication on dress materials.

X

Don Francisco was so absorbed in his picture that he would not leave it for a moment during the time when he was not at his office. Against everyone's advice he had left off his usual evening walk, and Don Manuel Pez, the friend who had generally accompanied him on it, began to come to the Palace instead so as not to lose the Bringuistic society altogether. The walk from the Ministry to the Palace and then up the Ladies' Staircase to the Second Floor was quite enough exercise to keep Don Manuel in health; and if he went out afterwards with Don Francisco or his wife to stroll up and down on the magnificent terrace which surrounds the great patio, he was assured of a good appetite for dinner as well.

The most affectionate urgings could not get Bringas away from his task while the daylight lasted. Neither pleadings, scoldings, nor threats of headaches and blindness could make him halt the feverish though orderly progression of his work. Pez sometimes stayed beside him talking about the political events of the time, but more often went out with Rosalía to walk up and down on the terrace. This walk was extremely pleasant, because the hollow of the building protected the terrace from the force of the wind without affecting the ventilation. Indeed the purest and best air from the mountains surrounds the Palace and its domestic city, situated as they are above the thick breath of the town.

This walk in such a monumental scene stirred the lady's fancy, awaking memories of those architectural backgrounds which Rubens and Vanloo and other painters put into their pictures, and which make the figures seem more important and give them an aristocratic air. Pez and Rosalía imagined themselves standing out elegantly against that background of balustrades and mouldings and stone carvings and urns, and this idea without their realising it compelled them to adopt a carriage and even a walk in keeping with the majesty of the scene.

This Pez (or as one would say in English; This Fish) was the most correct man that could possibly be found, and a perfect example of that sort of Civil Servant who is called 'higher' because he gets a large share in the division of the alms which the State doles out. In his looks and manners he seemed to symbolize the sovereignty of the government and to constitute one of the venerable props of the administration. He was very aimiable and well-bred, and his conversation though insubstantial was pleasing; for he could make some paradoxical comment on any subject that was introduced, however foreign to his bureaucratic experience. He had passed his whole life in political circles and had prolix information about contemporary politics, which on his lips turned into an endless series of personal anecdotes. He possessed the erudition of the more frivolous type of politician, and could manage a string of parliamentary phrases with amazing facility. Under all this foliage was hidden a complete scepticism as to principles and a faith in accomplished acts—a very common condition in those who have been nursed at the breast of Spanish politics, which are governed solely by accidents.

A man tanned inside and out and quite incapable of enthusiasm, Pez's face yet had in repose a look of peace which resembled that of the Saints who are enjoying Eternal happiness. In fact his face seemed to be saying: 'I have attained my desire.' It was the face of someone who does not mean to worry himself about anything or take anything seriously; and that after all is one way of resolving the great problem of life. For him the administration was simply a cloak of empty formulas created to cover up the working system of personal favours, the key to which lay in bribes and recommendations. No one could help his friends so effectively as Pez; it was this that gave him the reputation of being such a good fellow. And there was no one like him for getting on with everyone. Even among the revolutionaries he had his admirers.

His character was plainly visible in his attractive face. It was unwrinkled and admirably preserved, a little tanned and reddened by fresh air and exercise, like certain English faces. His fifty years seemed hardly more than forty, and were decorated with side whiskers and a moustache of dark gold slightly mixed with silver, both showing in their gloss and lustre that time at the dressing table had been consecrated to them. His eyes were pure Spanish eyes, so serene and gentle that they suggested the eyes Murillo painted when he was portraying St. Joseph. If Pez had let his beard grow and worn a tunic instead of a frock coat, and carried a spray of flowers, he would have been the living image of the Holy Patriarch, as the painters have represented him. Those eyes said to everyone who looked at them:

"I am the expression of that Spain which is sleeping beatifically, taking pleasure in being the plaything of events and never interfering in anything so long as she is allowed to eat in peace: the Spain which is not going anywhere, and expects nothing, living in the illusion of the present with a flowering spray in her hand: the Spain which submits to everyone who cares to command her, while professing a tame socialism; which does not understand ideas, or actions, or indeed anything except eating and digesting."

Pez dressed almost like a fashion plate; it was really a pleasure to observe such extraordinary neatness. His clothes had the quality of never getting stained or dusty and fitted him as if they had been painted on. Morning and evening he was dressed in the same way, in a broadcloth frock coat and trousers that looked as if they had been put on for the first time that day, and a white shirt which was always immaculate. And all without this neatness seeming in the least affected or suggesting that he took any trouble about it. As in the great stylists, this excessive finish seemed to be a natural facility, and his correctness almost a form of carelessness.

When he talked, people listened with pleasure and he evidently enjoyed hearing himself too, for he would look at the faces around him while he spoke to see what effect he was producing. His language was formed on the political style which has been created among us by the press and the tribune. His natural genius had been watered at the springs of amplification, so that he could not express any idea in precise terms but always presented it in triplicate. Here is an example: Bringas would say, without looking up from his work:

"What are they saying about the dismissal of the generals?"

And Pez would reply:

"At the point to which things have now come, friend Don Francisco, it's impossible, it's very difficult, at least, it would be very risky in fact to hazard any opinion. The revolution, which we've laughed at so much, joked about so often, jeered at so many times, is advancing, is mining its way underground, is cutting its path; and the only thing we can wish, the only thing we ought to ask for is that a complete incompatibility will not declare itself, a real war to the death, between these new ideas and the Throne, between the reforms which are indispensable and the person of Her Majesty."

XI

Pez and Rosalía, as has been said, used to go out and
walk up and down on the terrace together. The Rubens
nymph, full-fleshed and firmly rounded, and the spiritual
St. Joseph, in his frock coat and without his spray of
lilies, sublimated themselves against that architectural
background of white stone which resembles Tuscan
marble. She trailed her train along the smooth tiles set
in asphalt, while he walked with his left hand in his
pocket, gesticulating slightly with his right which held
his walking stick. At times some noise from the patio
drew their attention, and they would go to the balustrade.
It would be the coach of the little Infantas, perhaps,
taking them out for a drive, or the coach of the Minister
of State coming in. Sometimes the strollers would pause
in front of Doña Tula's windows, where acquaintances
inside would greet them with expressive movements of
their hands. Or they would stop to talk to Doña Antonia,
the Mistress of the Wardrobe, who was drawing her
Venetian blinds and watering her flower pots. Sometimes
some distinguished personage of the neighbourhood would
join them in their walk for a while: the wife of the
King's secretary, or the sister of the Second Majordomo,
or the Inspector General with his daughter—and then
they would all walk along together talking idly. But
when the two were alone together, the worthy functionary
would generally spend the time in confiding his troubles
to Rosalía: they had actually reached such a point as
seriously to disturb the serenity of his character.

For alas, the great Pez was not happy in his married
life. His wife had become intensely religious, and from

being sweetness itself, had grown terribly sharp tongued and simply impossible to get on with. Everything seemed to annoy her, and she was always quarrelling with someone. Though she was continually holding forth about moral perfection and had a perfect monomania about religious practices, her outbursts of bad temper and her inquisitorial attitude were perfectly insufferable; and months passed by without the husband and wife exchanging a single word. The house was like a club, there were such perpetual arguments going on in it and such disputes over the merest trifles.

"If it were only a question of the two of us," Pez declared. "I would try to bear it all patiently. But lately our children have taken to joining in violently."

The poor girls showed no inclination to follow in their mother's footsteps along the road to salvation. This was natural enough. They were young and enjoyed going out into society and going to the theatre; and there were scenes, sobs, weeping, over this incompatibility of worldly enjoyment and religious duties. Not a day passed without some domestic tempest, generally accompanied by fainting fits for which they had to call in the doctor and bring this, that, or the other drug from the pharmacy. Pez did his best to settle these disputes and persuade them to get on together, but he could do nothing. In the last resort he was always on the side of the poor girls, because he hated to see them made to spend all their time praying and carrying out stupid penances. If they were Christians and Catholics, what more could you ask? What was the point of trying to turn them into saints and martyrs at the pistol's point? For his part Don Manuel had always believed that the brake of religion was absolutely indispensable to society and Order. He had always defended Religion, and it seemed right to him that governments should protect it and persecute those who defamed it. He would even go so far as to admit as indispensable in

the political life of the time the affected piety of the
State. But private hypocrisy revolted him.

The worst thing of all, however, was Carolina's struggle
with her sons. The youngest was so small that he was
still tied to his mother's apron strings and consequently
spent his whole day in Church with a missal in his hand.
But Joaquin was twenty-two now, and was a lawyer,
a philosopher, an economist, a litterateur and reviewer.
How were you going to get him to confess and take
communion every week? Federico was very precocious
too and was writing articles on the *Mahabharata*. There
was a perfect cloudburst when either of the two youths
said anything that his mother considered sacrilegeous.
Christ, what scenes they had! Once when they were at
dinner Carolina got into such a rage that she pulled the
cloth off the table, breaking the plates and wine glasses
and spilling everything onto the floor, and then shut
herself up in her room and wept for three hours without
stopping. Little Rosa and Josefa, who had only come
out of short dresses the autumn before, were made to
go to confession every month. Poor innocents! What sins
could they possibly have to confess when neither of them
had even had an admirer yet?

And to cap it all the angry lady threw all the blame
for her offsprings' lack of religious feeling on Pez himself.
He was an atheist in disguise, she said, a heretic, a rationalist,
because he only heard mass on Sundays and then almost
from the doorway, talking all the way through it about
politics to Don Francisco Cucurbitas. He seemed to think
he'd done enough if he made a genuflexion when the
Host was raised, kneeled down on his handkerchief and
scribbled the sign of the Cross on his breast and forehead.
If that were all you were going to do you might as well
be a Protestant. In all the time they had been married
she had never once seen him go near the confessional.

His devotion was all outward show, carrying a candle in processions or sitting on the reserved benches when some bishop was consecrated.

In short the poor Pez was definitely not a fish in water, but a man who was tired of everything. And he knew who it was who had started Carolina off on this mystical housecleaning. It was that cousin of hers, Serafinita de Lantigua, who enjoyed such a reputation for sanctity. Frankly that cousin was a calamity! She and Carolina met each other in Church every morning at six o'clock and spent half the day there.

When she was at home Carolina sometimes laid down the comminatory style and took up the comparative; and then she would hold up the example of Luisito Sudre, the Tellerías' boy to her sons. He was a sucking saint, it seemed, and was already flagellating his tender flesh. While in these moods she was always attacking poor Pez too, telling him to examine himself in the mirror of Don Juan de Lantigua, that great Catholic, great litterateur and writer, a man as pious in theory as he was in practice, who never wrote a line that did not conform to the teachings of the Church. *His* Christianity was not a thing of rote, but sincere and heartfelt. There was a valiant upright man who was not ashamed of carrying out his religious duties in public and being seen kneeling for three hours together among the *beatas*. He was not like Pez and all the rest of that tepid crew, who only used religion as a ladder to help them reach high posts: not like those men who enrich themselves with the goods of the Church and then preach Catholicism in Congress, to deceive the fools around them, men with Christ on their lips and Lucifer in their hearts, who think that when they have given some of their small change to the Pope they have done all that is required of them. Farce! Comedy! Abomination!

71

In fact things had reached such a pass that Don Manuel had come to have a horror of his own home, and stayed in it as little as possible. There was no peace for him anywhere except in his office where he did nothing but smoke and receive his friends, and in the houses of a few of these friends, the Bringas' in particular. Oh, how he envied the peace of Don Francisco's hearth, and the harmony between the married pair. He had once been happy too, but now that was all over. *Et in Arcadia ego.* He was a pariah now, a dispossessed man. And he begged them to be kind to him and even spoil him a little to console him for the tormented life he led at home.

Pez would confide his troubles to Rosalía with great vehemence and she would listen with the liveliest interest and sympathy. Talking, always talking, they hardly felt the passing of the hours. And when the shade advanced out from the deep patio, full of a humid evening freshness, and the sky began to put out its pallid stars, Don Francisco would leave his troublesome hairs at last and come out, rubbing his eyes, to join them.

XII

After their cousin Augustin left for Burgos, the Bringas only went to the theatre very occasionally—in fact only when they were given tickets by friends who were not well enough to use them, or who had got tired of some play which had had too long a run. I can't remember now whether it was on Mondays or Tuesdays that Milagros was kind enough to be *At Home*. Don Francisco had always accompanied his wife to these evening gatherings, but after he had been working on his hair picture for a while he began to feel too tired at night to want to go out, and Rosalía had to go without him, only accompanied by Paquito. In May the promixity of examinations forbade the ambitious youth to neglect his studies and he only took his mother as far as the door and then returned to his books, Pez being charged with bringing the Señora de Bringas home at midnight or one o'clock. It is not very far from the beginning of the Calle Atocha to the Palace, and Pez generally spent the whole way intoning the jeremiad of his domestic troubles. Each night his stories became more distressing and moved warmer feelings of compassion in Rosalía's breast.

When she got back, Don Francisco would be in bed, his eyes and head tired out from reading two or three newspapers after he had finished his work on the cenotaph, and he would generally be asleep already, sometimes coughing a little or snoring. After she had gone to the children's room to make sure that they were not uncovered and that Isabelita didn't have one of her nightmares, Rosalía would undress in the matrimonial bedroom,

talking to her husband while she took off, first her outside clothes, then her petticoats and then that machine of
a corset from which her imprisoned flesh was visibly
reclaiming its liberty. Although she enjoyed going to
Milagros' *tertulias* extremely, the habit of trying to please
her husband made her say things about them which were
not at all what she really felt. However we can forgive
her for the sake of the marvellously exact judgements
which she pronounced on things and persons seen in the
Tellería salon.

"My dear," she would begin, "if you don't come with
me I'm not going there any more. You can't imagine
how that *tertulia* of Milagros' bores me . . . it's not the
place for me at all. And the things you see there! . . .
Really I can't help laughing sometimes. Poor Milagros
confides everything in me, and I know her difficulties
as well as if I were going through them myself. It really
is awful—I don't know how she has the face to receive
guests when she has no money to pay for anything. Tonight they only had a few trifles, really disgusting trash—
I would have been ashamed to serve it. Imagine what
those buzzards must say after they've left—all that
crowd who go to such houses only for what they can get
to eat. I never saw a woman with such nerve! When seven
was striking they still hadn't managed to get anything
to put on the *buffet*. They sent to the confectioners . . .
you can't help laughing . . . and the man wouldn't trust
them for twenty pounds of pastries. I don't know where
they got that ham in aspic which was all odds and ends,
or that boar's head which had such a horrid smell . . .
Really everything was disgusting . . . Everything, that is,
but the wine, that I must say was excellent. I wonder
where they got it from and who was the incautious person who let them have it. Poor Milagros was at her wit's
end—but how well she hides it, smiling at everyone.

And behind the scenes she's simply transformed, like a captain taking command in a shipwreck!"

Rosalía would grow indignant at this point.

"It's that wretch of a Marques who's to blame for everything! He's up to his eyes in debt, and the day when his creditors come down on him they won't leave him a shirt to his back. Milagros is an angel, poor thing— but you can't help admitting that she's terribly extravagant. If you gave her a thousand duros tomorrow she'd spend it all the same day, as if it were a hundred reals. I preach to her and draw up budgets for her, but it's all perfectly useless. Sometimes she seems to be trying to reform; but then she goes out and passes a shop and sees some dress material and *Farewell my money*! . . . She loses her head completely . . . Sometimes when I watch her shopping I really think she has a screw loose."

"And you can't help pitying the children. Tonight I was in Leopoldito's room, and really it reminds you of one of those cobblers' stalls in doorways. The walls are absolutely covered with grotesque pictures pasted on with seals, scenes of bullfights and caricatures from newspapers, really indecent. And everything in such disorder, and all smelling of drugs, because the boy is such a poor sickly creature. There were cheap paper-backed novels all over the room instead of school books and so many horse-whips and walking sticks that you could have set up a shop with them. The bed hadn't been made because the boy hadn't got up till six o'clock in the afternoon. And there he was limping about in all the mess, in broken boots, demanding something to eat, watching the sweets and cold meats being carried by in the passage, and making forays and grabbing things out of the dishes like a starving man!"

"Gustavo couldn't be more different, he's so polite and well brought up. He goes around from group to group in the *tertulia*, conversing with all the grown-up men in fine sounding phrases. In his little frock coat he always makes me think of those dolls of Scropp's—when he walks and talks you'd think he's been wound up with a key."

"Maria is really turning into a perfect beauty. Her mother won't bring her out yet because it would make her seem older herself. But it's a shame to see such a well developed girl—really she has a better bust than her mother—playing with dolls, and amusing herself with the maids, or copying out French exercises. Still the poor child had plenty to do tonight trying to keep her little brother's dirty hands out of everything and prevent him from sucking the sweets and licking the ices. I had a meringue that smelled of cod liver oil—Leopoldito's fingers had certainly been on it."

"But the Marques"—here she would grow indignant again. "If you didn't know him and only listened to what he said you'd think he was the most sensible man in the world. He talks all the time about what they've been saying in the Senate or what they are going to say there. What a flow of language! *He* could settle all the affairs of Spain if they would only let him; but as they won't, the country is going to the dogs."

"Milagros says he has taken to running after the maids lately, and she can't have one in the house that isn't a perfect fright. He can't bear me, because I refuse to understand his innuendoes. The truth is that he disgusts me, and I feel so sorry for Milagros. Poor woman, poor martyr! Her *mariducho*, as she calls him, keeps her so short of money that she has a terrible time trying to keep the house going at all. Really it isn't strange if the poor creature *has* indulged in a few distractions. It's not I who say so—I am only repeating what other people say—and even if I'm repeating it to you in confidence, that's not to say that I believe it, because you know ..."

But Don Francisco by now was sleeping soundly; as far away from all these miseries his wife was recounting, as the sky is from the earth.

XIII

Not all these confidences were on the same theme, for Rosalía's fertile imagination instinctively sought to give variety to these nocturnal doses of oral syrup with which she lulled her good man to sleep. With her mind always on the part she was playing, which demanded constantly increasing skill, since it grew more widely separated from the true expression of her character every day, she often pretended to be disgusted by things which in reality gave her only pleasure. For instance she would say:

"My dear, I thought our friend Pez would never finish telling me about his domestic troubles tonight! I am sorry for him, of course—but what a tiresome man he has become, he's a perfect hand-organ of lamentations. Carolina really is unpardonable; and she ought to mend her ways if only to spare us all this boredom."

Don Francisco always fell asleep before his wife, who sometimes remained wakeful and restless until far into the night, envying the quiet rest of the good man, who reposed on his thornless conscience like an angel on the clouds of Heaven. The ingenious lady did not find her conscience soft, but on the contrary hard and with sharp edges which kept her ill at ease all night. For her passion for dress had insensibly led her into a terrain which was bristling with dangers. For example she had to hide from her husband the acquisitions to her wardrobe which she was constantly making in ways so contrary to the economic traditions of Bringas. The drawers of her clothes-press were packed with pieces of material, some cut out and others waiting for the scissors, and an enormous round-topped trunk hid, with suspicious secrecy, dozens

78

of pieces of dresses, some old, some made over and some new; but all half finished and revealing a sudden interruption in the work on them when some unwanted witness was heard approaching. It was absolutely necessary to hide such things from the fiscal vigilance of Don Francisco, who put his nose into everything, and complained of a spool of thread that was not in his budget. Rosalía lay awake at nights trying to think up stories to make use of in case of surprise—but with what fictions could she possibly account for the great increase in the richness and variety of her wardrobe? Because that story about presents from the Queen was worn so threadbare that it couldn't be used again without danger.

And one day Don Francisco did return from his office earlier than usual and surprised Rosalía in the midst of all her things. She was working away in the *Camón*, as if she were in a modiste's workshop, assisted by a sewing woman she had got in to help her—indeed the *Camón* looked not so much like a workshop as like the back room of *Sobrino Hermanos*.

"But what on earth are you doing?" asked Bringas, in wonder.

There in front of him were twenty-four yards of *mozambique*, the checked kind at two pesetas a yard, a charming vaporous material in which Rosalía saw herself dressed every night in her dreams. This enormous length of material was spread out across the whole room and wound itself around the chairs, hung from the arms of the sofa, and lay along the floor waiting to be cut out by the sewing woman, who was on her knees in the middle of it consulting the fashion plate before she began. Lengths of silk and pieces cut on the bias into the strangest geometric shapes were lying on the trunk waiting to be cleverly combined with the *mozambique*. And the good Bringas also noticed pieces of shining silk of brilliant

colours scattered here and there about the room, like
bright touches not yet come from the palette, between
tangles of ribbon and pieces of embroidery.

The two women could not move without getting their
skirts caught in the *mozambique*, as well as in twenty yards
of navy blue poplin which had fallen off a chair and got
mixed up with the lengths of foulard. Out of this charming
disorder rose the special scent of drapers' shops, an odour
of dye and of paper and of the wood out of which packing
cases are made. On the sofa were half a dozen fashion
plates, showing in false colours those impossible ladies
who are as slim as flower stalks and as straight as posts,
and whose feet are no larger than fingers; ladies who have
an oblong crimson seal for a mouth, and who stand
gazing at each other with perfectly imbecile expressions.

Finding herself caught *in flagrante*, Rosalía's first impulse was to snatch everything up and hide it, but there
was no time; and her very fear suggested an easy way out
to her. It was a stroke of genius of that subtle intelligence.

"Hush, my dear," she said, putting her arm around
her husband's shoulder and drawing him gently out of
the *Camón*, so that the seamstress shouldn't hear what
she said.

"The fact is—I thought I'd told you about it yesterday—those dresses belong to Milagros. The poor thing had
the most dreadful quarrel with that brute of a Marques.
It was all about whether he spent more or she spent
more ... if you ... if I ... There was almost a tragedy.
I was beginning to think of sending for the arnica. Milagros
can't have anything made by Eponina any more because
her husband won't pay her bills; so she bought the
materials she needed and got a dressmaker in to make two
summer dresses for her—What could be more natural?
She was only going to use twenty-four yards of *mozambique* at two pesetas a yard and twenty yards of poplin

at fourteen—you see, nothing extravagant at all. Well, this brute comes in, probably fresh from losing hundreds of duros at cards, and as soon as he sees the materials and the dressmaker he begins to curse. Heavens, I was so astonished ... Then he began to turn everything over and stamp on the cloth and kick the fashion plates, all the time saying—well, I'd rather not remember exactly what he was saying—but it was all about how Milagros had ruined him with her wretched rags. Have you ever heard of such nonsense? Finally he stopped raging at his wife, and then he took the poor dressmaker by the arm and planted her in the street without even giving her time to put on her shawl. Did you ever hear of such a savage? Milagros fainted, and we had to give her all sorts of things to bring her round. In the end I had to bring the materials and the sewing-woman back here with me so that they could finish the dresses in peace. Milagros will come round later on to direct her, because I really don't understand these complicated styles. But Emilia, the girl who is working for her, is extremely clever and charges very little, and really she's almost as good as that famous Worth."

Satisfied with these ingenious explanations, the good man grew calm again; and as the Marquesa arrived soon afterwards and the three women shut themselves up in the *Camón* for the whole day, cutting out, measuring, trying on, and then altering and trying on again, Rosalía's story had all the appearance of truth. But she remained much preoccupied with the apparently insuperable difficulty of wearing her dresses for the first time—for against this visible evidence no explanation that she could think of would be of the slightest use. She could only console herself with the hope of an event which would provide an easy and safe solution to her problem. It was this. Gonzalez Bravo had offered Bringas the governership of a province. Pez urged him to accept the offer, saying that any province which was lucky enough to get such an honest and upright governor ought to leap for joy. But Bringas was repelled by the thorny and difficult nature of the appointment. He did not want to give up his tranquillity, and the obscure life in which he was so happy. However, if he should accept in the end, he would go off to his island alone, while his disconsolate wife would remain in Madrid at liberty to wear as many new dresses as she liked. Still, as it was more than probable that the great economist would refuse the post offered him, Rosalía continued to rack her brains trying to think of some way out of her net of deceits. In the end she found a formula which she thought would serve, and kept trying it over and over in her mind in preparation for the occasion when she would have to use it.

XIV

"You see, my dear, what happened was this—"

She began saying it to herself quite a month before the occasion for using the formula could possibly occur.

"I didn't want to annoy you by telling you about it at the time, for after all Milagros is our friend and the work was being done here in the house. But Emilia insisted on being paid in advance—pure stubbornness! Then suddenly, like a cannonball, Sobrino's bill for the materials. And poor Milagros couldn't pay either of them. You don't know what a state she got into. In the end I had to take the dresses off her hands for a third of their value; and I've been finishing them myself so as not to spend any more money on them. Really they were a gift, they were so cheap. And Emilia has been helping me with them and says that I can pay her whenever I like. You see . . ."

Thus the comedy was well rehearsed in advance for the occasion on which it would have to be performed. And meanwhile the work in the *Camón* went on unceasingly with much help from Milagros who came in every day bringing something new, or else with some happy idea which was the most recent inspiration of her fecund genius. She might say for instance:

"I mean to be splendid this summer. I'll tell you all my plans. The *Hijos de Rotonda* have let me have twenty five yards of *barège* quite cheap—Pilar San Salamo says that *barège* is being very much worn this year and I'm getting tired of *mozambique*. Well, I'm going to make it up very simply, with a really pastoral simplicity . . . just three frills and a trimming of narrow silk. The flounce will be embroidered and have bands of lace insertion, and the bodice will be embroidered in the same colour as the material ... The belt will be lilac coloured, fastened in front with a buckle ... You know I can't help thinking that this hat I'm wearing is too extravagant. I'm going to make myself another. I've got a shape I had last year, and if I use the velvet ribbons from this one I'll only need a plume and a *marabout* in the new style to put on the left side, like this ... "

In the beginning of May Rosalía was regretfully obliged to desert her delightful task because the doctor had ordered morning walks for Isabelita. The weather was so beautiful that it was like an invitation to sally out and enjoy the peaceful pleasures of the Retiro. So the lady began to take Isabelita and the little boy there every day; and after the first morning they were joined in their walk by the Señor de Pez, who was suffering, it seemed, from lack of appetite. Moreno Rubio had prescribed getting up early and drinking a large glass of water from the Egyptian Fountain, which is also called the Fountain of Health, and then walking about for a couple of hours before lunch.

And how the four of them enjoyed going into the reserved part of the garden, which was free to them because Rosalía belonged to the Palace. And what fun the children had in the Poor Man's House, and the Smuggler's Den, and the Persian House, and most of all throwing crumbs to the ducks in the Fisherman's House and climbing the spiral ascent to the top of the Artificial Mountain which is certainly the height of artificiality. All these Royal caprices, not to mention the Wild Beasts' House announce themselves at once as belonging to the epoch of Fernando VII, which, if it was an age of brutality in politics, in the arts was one of pure silliness.

Rosalía and Don Manuel became rejuvenated under the influence of the beauty of the vegetation and the

fresh air and the warmth of the May sun, and at times seemed almost as childish as the children. That is to say, they talked without thinking of what they were saying and no longer walked sedately, but sometimes quickly and sometimes very slowly, while the children played at hide and seek in the thick bushes. The glass of water, operating on the digestive processes of the good bureaucrat, produced the most marvellous effects. His vital functions were stimulated and he recovered his gaiety and talkativeness, while the instinct of gallantry was not left unaffected in this matutinal resurrection. Who could have imagined that a glass of water could produce such effects? Or that we have this simple remedy for our inveterate ills so often in our hands without making use of it? Pez's conversation passed easily from one subject to another and frequently turned to flattery, which in this case was well deserved. He praised the freshness and grace of the lady . . . how well she looked in everything she wore and how majestic her bearing was. Few people understood the art of dress as she did, or knew the secret of making everything they put on appear elegant. These puffs of incense almost suffocated Rosalía. What I am trying to say is that the depository of vanity (a certain bladder which conceited people have in their chests) grew so extraordinarily inflated that she could hardly breathe.

At the same time she felt a tickling desire to make certain confidences, but respect for her husband restrained her. In the end, however, Pez flattered her to such a pitch that indiscretion got the better of her prudence. I have seen them several times when they were returning from their walk, she laden with sprays of lilac, her veil pushed back a little as if she were sacrificing appearances to the freedom of country life, her face slightly flushed from walking, and also from the interest of the conversation; he carrying sprays of lilac too, transformed into a youth with ten years lifted from his shoulders, while the children ran about here and there, getting themselves dirty and muddy, breaking off twigs to beat each other with and leaping over the little water channels. Rosalía was talking—but who, except Pez himself, could catch her words, tinged as they were with a certain sadness, a gentle melancholy.

The poor creature, it seemed, could not make the most of herself by dressing to advantage, because her husband— Oh, she was never tired of repeating that he was the best man in the world, really perfect . . . But also there was no getting away from the fact that he was extremely stingy and kept her in a corner ill dressed and unnoticed. And it was not really for lack of money. Bringas had savings, he was always looking after the pennies. But he seemed to save simply for the pleasure of keeping his money in a box and taking it out and counting it from time to time. He was the best of men, a perfect husband and an excellent father; only he had simply no idea how to put his wife in the place which she ought to occupy in view of the positions which they both held. After all she had to mix with people of higher rank, with members of the nobility and the Queen herself. But Bringas was so close about money that he couldn't believe that she needed anything to wear except a woollen dress and some old-fashioned things long out of style. What she had suffered in trying to look nice, God alone knew. Because her husband went into absolutely everything—even the parsley they used in the kitchen went down in his account book. His poor wife had to be a perfect Newton to calculate the household expenses and save anything out of them to add to the wretchedly small amount that Bringas allowed her for dress. She had to work her fingers to the bone sewing and making over her clothes, because her husband went so closely into the accounts and into the reasons for the smallest expenditure that she couldn't hope to do more than save three reals a day out of the housekeeping money, or perhaps only two and a half or even nothing at all. These continual small annoyances made her life a martyrdom. And it wasn't that she wanted to be luxuriously dressed; but she considered that her own self-respect and the way in which she had to mingle with people of high rank imposed certain duties on her. She thought that she and the children ought not to go around looking shabby, considering the sort of houses which they visited. And she didn't want her friends to look at her contemptuously or whisper behind her back when they saw her in some skirt that had been patched or some old dress that was no longer in fashion. Nevertheless she was devoted to her husband, because apart from this meanness he was a man in a thousand. He was kind and affectionate and he had never had anything to do with disreputable women or placed a duro on a card in his life. And besides he had such an amiable disposition that so long as you didn't interfere with his financial arrangements you could do anything you liked with him. When she remembered this, she bore it all patiently—that is the difficulties she went through in trying to dress properly and not disgrace her high station.

From which it may plainly be seen that both the Señor de Pez and the Señora de Bringas had just cause of complaint in their married lives: he because of his wife's furious piety, and she because of her husband's meanness. Which only goes to show that no one is completely happy in this miserable world, and that it is rare to find two natures in complete accord within the matrimonial cage. For either the Devil, or Society, or perhaps God himself, mix up the pairs, so that all are discontented; and all in their separate cages are acquiring merits for Eternal Life.

XV

By the time the conversation had arrived at these philosophical reflections the little group would be coming out of the Retiro by the Glorieta Gate, and as they emerged into the streets they regained their composure. The children walked along quietly in front hand in hand, while the grown people ceased to exchange those confidences which seemed to be the fruit of outdoor enjoyments. It was like going from a free country to one where everything is regimented.

But when she was at home again, working in the *Camón* alone or with Emilia, the wife of Bringas would go over those confidences of the morning, and add to them things which had not then got past the frontiers of the mind.

"Pez is a *man*. At his side a woman of intelligence and fine appearance and aristocratic bearing could really show what she was made of and he is the man who had to draw that praying mule Carolina! But what woman, however attractive she was, wouldn't dwindle and fade when seen beside such an insignificant person as Bringas, a man who has no eyes for anything beyond trivialities, and is quite incapable of carving out a brilliant career for himself or of attaining a high position. What can you do with a man who is offered a province, and instead of leaping for joy begins to sigh and say that he prefers his carpenter's tools to a baton!

"But Pez—there is a man! And I know the woman he would have had if things ever went right in this world. A man like that needs a clever woman, one with fine manners, one who would make him seem more important by dressing herself to advantage, and would grow in

stature herself as she helped him to rise. Because the
secret of so many men's brilliant careers lies in the talent
of their wives. Paquito was saying only yesterday that
Napoleon would have been nothing without Josephine.
If Pez had had a wife who could bring together the most
important politicians of the day in her salon, instead of
that *beata* Carolina, he would be a Minister by now. And
I—if I were married to a man like that! But how could
anyone make a minister of Bringas?—a man who loses
his temper if he has to give a glass of sugared water to
a visitor, who would like to see me dressed in a nun's
habit and the children running around in rope soled
shoes—the miserly creature! Oh, Pez, if you had the
wife you should have had, you would never let her go
out into the streets looking like a scarecrow to make you
ridiculous. That stupid husband of mine should take
lessons from a man who lives on a salary of 50,000 reals
as if it were 12,000 duros in rents, and pays 24,000 reals
a year just for his house. And it's not that Pez has debts,
only that he knows how to manage and make the most
of his opportunities. But Bringas could never do that—
a man who spends three hours lecturing me as to whether
I should or shouldn't put seven more beans in the stew.
A man like that cannot possibly understand such things;
he doesn't look beyond his tiny salary and is afraid
they'll give him a decoration because he'd have to buy
the insignia for it! He won't even let them make him
governor of a province! And now he objects to my
getting two more buckets of water from the water
carrier—he thinks if you wet your palms that's enough.
And he thinks that I don't need more than eighteen
yards of material for a dress; and he wouldn't let me get
Ottoman ribbons to trim my house dress with, and tried
to make me use the yellow ribbons from the boxes of
cigars Augustin used to give him . . ."

91

There were evenings when the weather was too bad for Pez and Rosalía to go out on the terrace, and then the three of them spent the time talking in *Gasperini* instead. And you should have heard the eulogies which Don Manuel pronounced on his friend's stupendous work on these occasions! Standing beside him with one hand in his pocket and gnawing his moustache, he let his critical gaze rest on the marvellous glass, as peopled with hairs as a human head and as shining as if it had just left the dressing table.

"But it's really marvellous—what hands you have, and what patience! It ought to go straight into a museum!"

And at the same time he was saying to himself, gnawing his moustache more fiercely, and thrusting his hand deeper into his pocket:

"Really, there never was such a ridiculous object. No head but yours could have produced it! Idiot! No one but you thinks up such horrors, and no one but my wife admires them—you were made for each other."

One day Don Francisco left his work more tired than usual. He was inclined to see double too, and felt as giddy as if he were on board a boat. But he insisted that it was only a temporary disturbance and congratulated himself on the beautiful effect of the picture. The angel was completely finished, with all those incredible molecules of hair in place. The willow hung its weeping branches over the tomb—and it was a pity, Bringas could not help thinking, that people never have green hair, for if he could have got hold of some the illusion would have been complete. The background was finished too, and was a model of melancholy in perspective, carried to such a point that no one who was not extremely hard-hearted could look at it without wanting to weep. The flowers on the ground were still to do, as well as all the foreground. Bringas had decided at the last moment to put

some broken and fallen columns there to suggest a temple
in ruins, as a finishing touch to this scene of desolation.

The beginning of June saw most of this work completed; but there were still a few things to be done—
small sunflowers and large pansies, and a number of black
butterflies to be put in here and there, sipping the sweet
Macassar from the calices of those piliform flowers. At
just about this time various events occurred of which
our artist remained in ignorance, but which nevertheless
must be related here. One was that as the day approached
on which Torres would be coming for his money, Rosalía
became so depressed that anyone might have supposed
she had been robbed, or had suffered some other un-
common injury. She spent her time in endless calculations;
but the numbers would never add up to the figure she
required. What could she do? Should she go to the
Señor de Pez? Oh, if she knocked at that door, she would
certainly be heard! But she could not bring herself to
do it. And in any case, Don Manuel had gone to the baths
at Archena (without two courses of treatment every
year he was a lost man, he said) and would not be back
before the twentieth of the month.

On the twelfth Torres appeared, with those eyes
shaped like hard boiled eggs and full of a sort of astonished
gentleness. He was the image of amiability—always sup-
posing that one could keep ones amiability while being
garrotted. His cloying smile affected Rosalía like a mias-
matic fluid, which filtered into her and made her feel ill.
How impertinent that small nose looked, and what an
irritating habit that was he had of sucking his beard as
if he were trying to get some nourishment out of it! In
fact this rather handsome man, who had always been an
object of perfect indifference to Rosalía, seemed to her
now like a good-looking executioner who had arrived
with the rope.

93

XVI

And he was so insistent. On the fourteenth he must have the money without fail. He couldn't wait a day or even an hour for it, because his honour would be compromised with Mompous if he didn't have it then. And if Rosalía couldn't fulfil her undertaking, he would be obliged to ask Don Francisco for it.

"For God's sake—don't think of doing such a thing", stammered the wife of Bringas in horror.

And she cast up her accounts again for the hundredth time. But even if she sold things that she didn't want to sell, she couldn't get such a sum together. The second-hand clothes dealer had brought her a certain amount of money, but she had spent it on little things for the children. If Milagros would only give her back the seven hundred reals she had borrowed to pay the jeweller—but she *must* give it back; Rosalia would ask her for it outright. Or if by some art of the Devil or—what was much more probable—some miracle of Her Divine Majesty, Cándida should have some money! Cándida owed her five duros which Rosalía had lent her one day 'so that she needn't change a bill for a hundred escudos'. Those strayed reals must return to the fold.

With a sudden access of energy she started off at once to see Milagros. But as ill luck would have it the Marquesa was at a religious function which she and some other ladies had got up and were paying for. It was a Novena dedicated to some titular saint or other, with *Manifiesto*, Stations of the Cross, sermon, *Novena*, Glorification of the Saint and so forth. Rosalía was so anxious to see her friend as soon as possible that she decided to go to the service too. The street outside was full of elegant coaches, and the church was gorgeous with velveteen, decorations of gilded paper, innumerable lamps and enormous bunches of artificial flowers, as well as tent shaped curtains which looked as if they had been borrowed for the occasion from some third-rate theatre. There were so many people present that it was difficult to get in at all, but Rosalía managed to shove her away in among the elegant crowd. However, she still could not reach the Marquesa, who had got herself into the presbytery with the priests.

Time went by; and Rosalía heard half-a-sermon, which was pathetic and flute-toned, a dish of commonplace ideas served up with a sauce of theatrical gestures; and after that some rather nasal chanting. In the end it grew so late that she was obliged to leave without seeing Milagros at all. For the unfortunate Señora de Bringas was a martyr to her husband's punctuality, and could never be late in returning home. If the meal was not on the table exactly on time, Don Francisco grumbled and made disagreeable remarks such as:

"My dear, I am positively weak with hunger. Another time, if you are going to be late, do let us know beforehand, and we will eat without you."

Rosalía spent that night very uneasily; and the next day, which was the 13th of June, was just setting out again to see her friend when the Marquesa herself appeared at the door in a state of great distress. This was evident not only in her neglected appearance, but in her changed voice and other uncontrollable symptoms. Rosalía shared this alarm when Milagros said to her:

"Oh, my dear, I'm in such difficulties. If you can't help me ..."

"I!" exclaimed Rosalía, starting back from her as she realised that this was another financial crisis like her own.

"What a moment for you to come to me . . . If you only knew . . . I was just coming around to see you."

"To see me? I'll tell you what has happened so you'll take pity on me. Tomorrow I'm giving a ball and a supper. It's a family occasion . . . absolutely indispensable. I've already sent out the invitations . . . My dear, for heaven's sake, give me a glass of water—I can't breathe, something seems to be choking me here . . ."

She drank a few sips of water and continued:

"Well, to save myself trouble I ordered the whole supper from Bonelli, and yesterday I asked him to come around to see me about the final arrangements. And do you know what happened? The man had the impertinence to insist on my paying for the three suppers I'd already had from him before he would supply another. I would have done it willingly enough if I could have— you can imagine how much I enjoy owing money to tradesmen . . . Oh, believe me, my *mariducho* is to blame for the way we live! But to go on—what was I saying? As I could do nothing with Bonelli, I sent for Tronchin from the Calle del Arenal—I'd never dealt with him before. And we'd agreed on the price and settled everything, and then—what do you suppose? Very courteously and in a very roundabout way the wretched man gave me to understand that he wouldn't serve the supper unless I paid for it in advance. Really, it was an insult; such a thing has never happened to me before. The truth is that all the caterers are in league together, and Bonelli had told Trochin that I owed him for three suppers. It's a conspiracy against me, a plot . . . Although, of course, looked at from their point of view you can't blame them, can you, dear? But how am I to blame either? It's all that wretched husband of mine! Whatever they say about him is too little; you simply can't slander him. Yesterday I had to pay his tailor's bill for him—

they'd tied it to the doorbell. Well, that is the situation—advise me, show me some way out of it."

Rosalía modestly declared herself incapable of helping her friend out of this labyrinth she had got herself into, more especially as she was in a similar predicament herself and had counted on getting the—well, the seven hundred reals . . ."

"Oh yes, I remember about it of course. Only the day before yesterday I'd put the money in my pocket-book to bring to you, but—you must forgive me—before I could get out of the house the Collector for the Congregation came round with the receipt for my share of the expenses of the function yesterday, and I was obliged to give the money to him. I saw you in Church, didn't I? I wish you had been near me so we could have talked. The ceremony was beautiful, I thought. But there were certainly some absurd sights. Did you see the Señora de Cucurbitas in that extraordinary tobacco-coloured dress of hers, like the habit of some order of tobacco sellers, or the uniform of the shop? And Pilar San Salamo was dressed in a very extreme way too. I never in my life saw such an enormous *pouf*. And although they do say that bustles are getting larger all the time, I think the Church expects you to observe some sort of moderation in things like that. As for myself—were you close enough to see me properly? I couldn't have been more simply dressed . . . But to come back to my difficulties—can't you advise me? Think for me, I don't know what I am doing any more. If I don't find some way out between now and tomorrow I am lost. Really, I think I will kill myself."

Rosalía, merely from curiosity, asked her friend how much she needed, and when she heard that the sum required was nine or ten thousand reals, her face showed so much annoyance that it increased the distress of the already much distressed Milagros.

"Oh, how little encouragement you give me! And to crown it all, Eponina made such a scene yesterday afternoon . . . These things never happen to other people. She has sent in such bills . . . absolutely exhorbitant . . . Just for making a dress, two thousand reals! And for the trimmings on this dress I'm wearing, just for the trimmings fifteen hundred reals. Really, she ought to be shot."

"Ten thousand reals!" Rosalia muttered, looking at the floor, and counting the syllables one by one as if they were coins. "With a fifth of that I would have enough."

"Perhaps Don Francisco . . .?" Milagros suggested with animation, conveying the idea that Bringas surely must have savings.

"Hush, for heaven's sake! If my husband even heard of it . . . These things drive him out of his mind."

"What about Cándida?"

"*Ave Maria Purisima!*"

"There's one thing that I forgot to tell you. I can get four thousand by pawning some things, so I'll only need six."

"Oh, it's impossible, absolutely impossible."

"This Torres . . ." whispered Milagros, her mouth so dry that her tongue was cleaving to her palate.

"Jesus! Torres! . . . What madness!" exclaimed Rosalía, seeing the image of her creditor rise before her like a fantastic apparition. "I don't know whether I told you that tomorrow before twelve . . . Oh, it was madness to buy that mantle. You see what has come of it! What ever made me let myself in for all this wretchedness!"

"But that's the merest trifle, dear," declared the Marquesa, with that tone and air of indulgent superiority which she knew how to put on when it suited her. "If I get safely through my troubles, this trifling sum you're worrying so much about shall go down to my account."

She came closer, and took her friends's arm.

"Don Francisco must have plenty of money locked up somewhere—absolutely unproductive money, just gold pieces piled together. And it's so old-fashioned! They say that that's why the country is in the state it's in, because capital doesn't circulate, and all the gold and silver is locked away in chests, not benefitting anybody, not even its owner. Don Francisco is evidently one of those people who think money is meant for growing spider webs. In this one point your admirable husband is like the rich villagers. Why don't you suggest to him that he ought to lend me the money I need? It's understood, with interest, of course, and a proper agreement . . . I don't want . . ."

"I doubt whether Bringas . . ."

But the Marquesa interrupted her with warmth:

"Surely, my dear, you must have some influence over him! . . . Really, it's too much! If you said to him: 'My dear man, for the love of God, this money isn't bringing anything in—' and spoke sharply, so that he'd listen to you. Haven't you any strength of will? I always imagined that he consulted you about everything, and let you dominate him, as you have so much more intelligence and ability. Do at least make the attempt. And in case it comes off, your little bill shall be put to my account.—Consider it as a commission," she added laughing.

"I can't believe that my husband—Oh, it's impossible!"

However, impossible as she thought her friend's idea to be, she could not help meditating upon it. The very difficulty of the undertaking attracted her spirit, as great problems are apt to fascinate superior minds. For a time there was no sound to be heard in *Gasperini* except Rosalía's sighs, and an occasional small cough from the Marquesa who had a tendency to bronchitis.

The two friends had the apartment to themselves, for Bringas was still at the office and the children had not returned from school, so they could discuss their troubles freely without making any mystery of them. The Marquesa kept returning to her proposition and bolstering it up with weighty arguments (Unused money is the cause of the backwardness of the Nation!) and with clever flattery. But Rosalía persisted in considering her suggestion as one of the most arduous and difficult undertakings which could be demanded of the human will; merely to attempt it would be an essay in heroism. They were still sitting in the same state when Cándida appeared, smiling and pompous. She had been visiting Her Majesty and Doña Tula, and thus had gone down to the kitchens, and the Chef had insisted on her accepting three *entrecôtes* and two partridges. "Galland does these things . . ." He was always making her presents, and so as not to seem unappreciative, she had said "Well, let them be sent up to my apartment, then."

"Later on I'll send you a partridge and two *entrecôtes*.— No, don't thank me. I shouldn't touch them anyway—I have too much meat already. Yesterday I divided a magnificent loin among my neighbours. I'd ordered it from the Plaza del Carmen because I was expecting some guests to dinner. If you'd seen how grateful the poor people were! My house is the Palace Almshouse. . . . The day I leave that quarter a great many tears will be shed."

And then, carrying her ideas to a region very distinct from charity, she let fall the following words which are set down here exactly as she pronounced them:

"Could either of you tell me how or where I could place some money at interest, some that I don't need at the moment? I'd want something safe, and something that paid a reasonable interest, of course."

XVII

The effect which these words had on the two friends was not as great as might have been expected. Rosalía's face only showed an indifferent incredulity, which soon turned into alarm as she remembered that Cándida's borrowing of five duros the month before had been preceded by a similar preamble. Milagros, on the other hand, while having no confidence in what Garcia Grande's widow said, suspected that there *might* be something in it—or perhaps it was only that she seized on anything, however absurd, as a drowning man clutches at straws.

"But tell me, Cándida ... You actually have this money?"

"Don't be so literal, child, ... I haven't got it in my pocket at this moment, if that's what you mean, but it's just the same as if I had. Muñoz and Nones are going to pay it to me some day soon."

"Some day soon ... Yes ..." It was spoken sadly.

"And as I'm accustomed to planning things well in advance ... Frankly, I don't like to have large sums in the house; even in the Palace there are undesirable people."

Without giving much heed to Cándida's projects for investing her money, Milagros was observing her dress. At this epoch the illustrious widow was visibly going downhill, both in her bearing and in the cleanness and neatness of her clothing, though she had not yet reached—and not by a long way—the pitiful extreme of abandonment at which she arrived later on. But just then the children came in from school and Rosalia went out to give them their lunch.

"How charming Isabelita is!" said Cándida.

And she went off to the dining room, leaving the Marquesa alone with her melancholy. Through the open door she could hear the children's chatter, and the voice of their mother scolding them for being so impatient and the noise of the kisses that Cándida was giving them. Before long Rosalía came back to *Gasperini* alone, and Milagros saw that she was frowning and smiling at the same time, as we do when we cannot help being amused by one of those comic incidents which often occur on the saddest occasions.

"Do listen to this," she whispered in her friend's ear. "While we were in the dining room Cándida asked me with much secrecy if I could lend her five duros."

Milagros smiled wanly, like a sick person making an effort to distract herself, but soon fell back into the deep sadness which was wearing her away like a consumptive fever. A picture kept passing through her mind, an image of the terrible scene that would occur on the following evening—the guests coming in, the rooms full of people, she in her great skirt of rose coloured silk with its enormous *pouf* and very long train pretending to be gay—and all the time the problem of the supper still unsolved. Because on an occasion like that it would be impossible to serve a few trifles. How disgraced she would be!

Rosalía saw her friend's eyes fill with tears and wanted to console her, but "That spendthrift, that useless wretch . . ." was all she could think of to say.

Don Francisco came in soon afterwards, less lively and cheerful than usual. Milagros greeted him in the most affectionate manner, and then began to complain of her hard fate, how inexorable God was with her, piling trouble upon trouble. Bringas tried to comfort her as best he could with Christian reasonings, for although he had long kept a certain feeling of spite against her, because she had not sent him the Christmas present he thought she should have given him that time he mended her marble casket, he had almost come to the point of pardoning the offence, though he could not forget it. Then to tell the truth he did not much care for his wife's intimacy with the Marquesa, even if it was confined, as he thought, to a mutual interest in dress.

"Won't I have the pleasure of seeing you at my house tomorrow?" Milagros asked.

But Don Francisco excused himself politely, only longing as he spoke to get back to his great work. He had begun to notice, he said, that going out at night didn't seem to agree with him. He suffered a good deal with his head, he thought it must be nerves, perhaps the weather had something to do with it too; the sky had been so overcast lately, as if it were full of water that wouldn't fall. His chief at the office thought that it must be his digestion, and recommended taking a colocynth pill with his meals; but he had such a dislike of chemists' shops that he couldn't bring himself to take anything. He feared, however, that his indisposition would deprive him of the pleasure of coming to Milagros' soirée, and that he would be obliged to content himself with reading the accounts of it which the papers would carry the following day.

"Oh, I don't know what will happen," the poor woman said, with lugubrious sadness. "Perhaps there won't be any soirée. Such terrible things have been happening to me lately—Forgive me if I don't say any more, I really don't want to talk about it . . . My husband is a—but I should be the last person to talk about the things he does; and in any case they are only too well known unfortunately. Don't laugh at me if you sometimes see me in tears. There are certain things—"

Bringas hardly knew what to say. He got rid of her in the end with a warm handclasp and an affectionate *Hasta Mañana*. In the drawing room and afterwards in the passage the two friends continued to whisper together for a while.

"I have prepared the ground a little" Milagros said, in a tone of agony. "Now *you* must try. Don't be afraid, surely . . ."

"My dear, you are mad. You are dreaming."

"Then there is no way out for me," murmured the unhappy woman, embracing her friend and drawing her closely to her.

Much moved, Rosalía found nothing to say.

"At least," the Marquesa said brokenly, "tell him what has happened. God might touch his heart."

"I'll tell him as soon as Cándida goes. But if you knew how little hope I have . . . I might as well say it—I haven't any. And I—what about me? I am in just as much trouble. What can I do between now and tomorrow morning? . . . But—it has just occurred to me—why don't you ask your sister to help you?"

"My dear, you don't know what you are saying. I can't ask my sister, she has helped me so many times already. I've made use of her so often, I can't do it again. And anyway I couldn't do it now. We had an argument a few days ago. Rather than go to my sister, I'd go to Her Majesty and throw myself at her feet . . ."

"Yes, yes, do that . . . It's the best thing you can do . . ."

"No, no, no . . . I believe that I shall die of grief before morning. Is the chapel open? I'll go in and pray for a while. Perhaps God will enlighten me. I'll come back tomorrow to see if there is any hope."

Rosalía's discouraged face showed clearly that any such hope was only a dream of that scheming mind. And it should be remarked at this point that the sadness which the Señora de Bringas exhibited was caused much more by the thought of her own difficulties than by those of her esteemed friend. She had such faith in Milagros' remarkable abilities that she said to herself 'I don't know how she'll do it, but she'll manage somehow.' And when the Marquesa clasped her hand for the last time, Rosalía said to her:

"Tomorrow you'll tell me how you've arranged it all."

When she went back to Bringas' niche to try to tell him about the Marquesa's difficulties, he took the wind out of her sails by saying sarcastically before she could begin:

"What is the Tellería in such a state about today? The same old thing, her terrible lack of money? I suppose there is no one left silly enough to trust them for two reals worth of anything; the supply of fools must be getting exhausted, they have had such repeated shocks."

Rosalía's lips were sealed; she dared not say a word. Nailed on her mind, like an INRI, was the image of Torres and the fatal figures of the sum which he must be paid. To confess her need of money to her husband would be to confess at the same time a whole series of clandestine inroads on that domestic economy which was Bringas' second religion. But if God did not send some solution, she would be absolutely obliged to unburden herself and take the consequences, which would certainly be dreadful. No, never. O Christ, she must think of something; she must turn everything over in her mind again, get inside the very heart of the problem and find the key to it. Before she would let her husband into the secret of her purchases, which were perhaps the principal delight of her dull and quiet life, she would choose rather to sacrifice all her beautiful things, to tear out those pieces of her heart which were embodied in the visible world in the form of cloth and embroidery

105

and ribbons, and throw them to the voracious maw of the second-hand clothes dealer; to be sold for next to nothing. It was heroism that was required of her, not tears.

Brooding over these ideas, she retired to the *Camón* to think over the situation again, for her mind always seemed to be clearer when she was there. Cándida, after amusing herself with the children for a while had gone in to talk to Bringas while he worked, and Rosalía could hear them from the sewing room, though she could only catch a word here and there, such as "role of the State ... consolidation ... revolution ... generals ... the Canaries ... Montpensier." It was evidentthat they were talking of high affairs of state and low politics.

Suddenly there was a violent crash, as if a piece of furniture had fallen, breaking the floor tiles; and after this sudden noise a cry from Bringas—but such an agonized cry that Rosalía was struck cold and breathless and completely unable to move. What could have happened? Had the domed ceiling fallen on the best of husbands?

XVIII

In a moment Rosalía recovered from this paralysis caused by the sudden shock and her alarm, and ran towards *Gasperini*. But when she got there, what she saw was perfectly incomprehensible to her. Bringas was standing in the middle of the room, with his face contorted and terribly pale; his hands were clenched and his eyes were wide open—extraordinarily wide open. The little table which stood beside his big work-table and held his jar of lacquer and the alcohol lamp to heat it, had been turned over, evidently when the artist had sprung up suddenly from his chair; and the spilled spirit was running along the carpet burning with vaporous flames. Cándida was busily engaged in trying to put these out by stamping on them. She had pulled her skirts up to her knees and was jumping up and down wherever the flames were fiercest. But as the hot lacquer had been spilled at the same time and is one of the stickiest of substances, the soles of the old lady's shoes kept adhering to the floor so firmly that she had to make great efforts to lift them up again.

Rosalía ran straight to her husband; and he clutched her to him with convulsive anxiety when he felt her near him, and turned his eyes in every direction, as if he were looking for something that was escaping from him. His face expressed such terror that his wife could not remember ever having seen anything like it.

"Oh, what is it?" was all that she could say in utter consternation.

Bringas rubbed his eyes and opened them wide again, opening and closing his eyelids in an unnatural manner, and then exclaimed in a heartrending tone:

"I can't see! I can't see!"

Rosalía could not speak: she was too appalled. But the Señora de Garcia Grande, who had managed to put out the fire though her shoes were still sticking to the floor as she walked, hurried to the aid of the pitiful pair.

"It's not anything serious," she said, noticing Don Francisco's strange stare.

"Where is the window?—the window?" groaned the unhappy man in desperation.

"It's here, here—can't you see it?" cried Rosalía, turning him towards the light.

"No, I can't see it, I can't see you, I can't see anything at all ... It's all dark ... perfectly black ..."

"Oh, that cursed work ... I told you how it would be ... everyone told you so ... But it won't last ..."

Rosalía was more dead than alive, and could not think what to do; she was helpless with misery. Cándida, who was naturally less affected, took command of the situation.

"We'll put him on the sofa," she said "and then we must get the doctor."

Between them they led Don Francisco to the sofa, and he fell down upon it in despair, as if they were letting him fall into his coffin. He kept feeling the objects around him and touching his wife, who did not separate herself from him by even an inch.

"Oh, I told you what would happen!" she repeated, drowned in tears, and trying to hide the change in her voice. "Oh, that wretched hair picture ... working all day ... if you noticed that your eyes were tired, why did you go on with it?"

"My children—where are my children?" Bringas whispered.

Isabelita and Alfonsin were standing in the doorway afraid to come any nearer. The little boy still had the bread he had been eating for lunch in his hand and was

108

slowly chewing a piece of it; while the little girl, her hands clasped on her shoulders and her face very serious, was standing and staring in consternation at the sad group her parents made. Rosalía called them in; and Bringas felt them all over and kissed them a great many times, lamenting that he could no longer see them and prophesying that he would never see them again. The poor man shed more tears in that quarter of an hour than he had shed in his whole previous life. And Rosalía, when she considered this sudden misfortune with which God had afflicted them, thought that it must be a punishment for the faults she had committed.

Finally they had to take the children away. Prudencia took charge of them and promised to keep them with her and not let them come in again. There was a danger that Isabelita might be too much affected by the painful scene and have a worse attack of her malady than any she had had as yet. Meanwhile the Señora de Garcia Grande, who was always particularly helpful and attentive to her friends on critical occasions, did everything that she could think of to make herself useful.

"I'll go for the doctor myself," she said. "And you'll find that he'll say it's nothing serious. I had something similar happen to me once when I was learning to make Flanders-point. Suddenly I felt some very peculiar sensations in my eyes and then I began to see objects divided into two halves. It all ended in a terrible headache —an ophthalmic headache, they call it. And I remember my doctor said that he'd known cases that lost their sight completely for a few hours, or even a few days. Try to be calm, Don Francisco. Drink a glass of water with a little wine in it. I will be back as soon as possible."

She bustled out quickly, with a sincere desire to help her friends; and as she did not find the doctor who lived in the Palace at home, went out to look for another.

When they were left alone together Bringas and his wife hardly exchanged a word. She could not stop gazing at him continually, hoping that at any moment those staring eyes might recover the precious faculty for which they were created. An occasional word, and the sighs and lamentations of the poor patient were the only sounds to be heard in that sad scene, most eloquent when most mute.

The doctor came at last, accompanied by Cándida, who had insisted on bringing him back with her. He was an affable old man, very much of the antique school, an excellent diagnostician, but timid about prescribing; and it was said not very lucky with his patients. When he heard the history of the case, he diagnosed it as Retinal Congestion.

"The retina—" Cándida agreed. "That won't last long. You'll soon recover your sight. But that hair picture— my friend, you must never touch that again."

"Oh, I told you so, I told you it would be all right." Rosalía exclaimed joyfully, recovering her spirits with the hopes the doctor held out to them. "But what should we do for him?"

The doctor prescribed absolute rest and a special diet with various medicines. He also told the patient to wear a black bandage over his eyes and advised a sleeping draught if he could not sleep that night; and he offered to come in early the next morning to examine the injured eyes more carefully. It was growing late and the last rays of daylight were sadly withdrawing from the apartment. But when the kind old man left, Bringas and his wife were in a much more cheerful mood.

"It's nothing, children, you needn't be alarmed," Cándida told them comfortingly. "Go to bed and sleep if you can. There's nothing to be frightened about. All that's necessary is quiet and a little patience. I'll go for the medicines now and get anything else you need at the same time. And I'll be only too glad to stay the night if you want me to."

When the helpful old lady returned from the chemist's with the medicines, Rosalía had already put her husband to bed, after bandaging his eyes with a large piece of black taffeta. Like all cases of incipient blindness, Bringas pretended not to need any assistance in undressing himself; and knowing how distressed his wife was, made an heroic effort to cheer her up by talking hopefully and affectionately, as he if were the healthy person and she the patient.

"I expect this trouble will go away soon, but it's certainly very unpleasant—it's no joke not being able to see! But you may be sure I'll be patient about it; I'm almost getting accustomed to not seeing already. Anyway, I'm glad I don't have to call in an oculist. Even if they cure you, those people want an eye out of your head for doing it."

The night passed uneventfully except that Bringas was restless and had a neuralgic pain in his head and eyes. Rosalía sat up, sharing her attention between her blind husband and her epileptic child. Fortunately Cándida spent the night with them, comforting her afflicted friend by her mere presence and also aiding her in all sorts of practical ways. For she was a great help on such occasions, being a perfect mine of information on every point of medical treatment. She could think of some solution for every difficulty and never lost her head; while her old bones seemed incapable of weariness.

At dawn Rosalía was overcome by sleep as she sat in her chair beside her husband, who had fallen into a sort of lethargy at last. But no sooner had she dozed off than she saw Torres, with that beard and that nose, and saw too the sum she required, which seemed to run before her digit after digit, unrolling its particles in dilated space; she saw too the appointed hour of that day now opening so menacingly ... The unhappy woman started awake and opened her eyes; she thought that she had heard her husband moan; but it must have been an illusion, she realised, for the good man seemed quite tranquil and his regular breathing showed that he was really asleep at last.

"Torres ... the money!" Rosalía thought, rubbing her head to drive the idea away, as if it were a fly that had lighted on her forehead. "And my God, in such circumstances!"

XIX

But almost at the same moment that she was thinking this there flashed through her mind—like one of those celestial rays of which the mystics tell us—a saving idea, an easy solution to her problem; and one which was derived—how strange life is!—from the very situation in which the wretched family found itself.

She got up from her chair as quietly as possible so as not to wake the patient, and went out of the room, pausing a great many times on the way. She knew what to do: it was perfectly simple. What she could not have done on the previous day, she could easily do on this melancholy morning. She had often looked at the silver candlesticks speculatively, but realised that it would be impossible to pawn them without their absence being noticed by the lynx-eyed Don Francisco. Now she could do it in perfect safety. Only she would have to get the money together to redeem them as soon as possible; then her husband need never know anything about it even after he had recovered his sight—please God and Santa Lucia that that would be soon! The candlesticks might not provide enough money since, besides the sum for Torres, she had the other half of Sobrino's bill to pay, so she decided to pawn the diamond earrings that Augustin Caballero had given her, too. Bringas would not be able to see that she did not have them on, and if he did by chance notice their absence when he passed his hand over her face, she would make some excuse—she would say that she had taken them off because she was not in the mood for wearing such things.

Luckily she had in Doña Cándida just the person for such delicate financial undertakings. Rosalía found her in the dining room as lively and active as if she had slept all night, and brought out the chocolate so that the old lady could make it for herself the way she liked it. And while her friend was doing this with the careful attention that such a pleasant task deserved, Rosalía explained her project to her. For some time a low whispering could be heard in the room; and Cándida's head made so many affirmative movements that it would have given a feeling of security to doubt itself.

"Don't worry: the money shall be here before twelve. On these occasions I employ a friend of mine, a perfect lynx. He is trustworthy, secret and active, and understands everything about it—and he does it all before you can say Jesus."

There are, however, reasons for believing that by this period, which was in the second stage of her decadence, Cándida had begun to visit the pawn shops and money lenders herself, either on her own behalf, or else performing this delicate service for some particular friend. Maximus Manso called this the *Second Manner of Doña Cándida;* and it should be said that there was a *Third Manner* which was still more lamentable.

Everything was done as easily and as quickly as Garcia Grande's widow had promised, and it was not quite 11.30 when she came back with the money. Rosalía took it anxiously and rejoiced when she found that there was enough to pay both Torres and Sobrino and still have something left over for any unusual expenses that might occur.

"I don't know how to thank you!" she said to her worthy friend, pressing her hands warmly. "The things shall come back to the house as quickly as possible though, for I don't like to have my possessions making these journeys . . . only in a great emergency . . ."

It is difficult to say how the conversation turned onto the subject of a certain little money difficulty which Cándida found herself in just then, due to the slowness of her wretched man of affairs . . . It was a matter of three or four days . . .

How could Rosalía refuse this favour to someone who had helped her so much? But she felt as if she were tearing out a piece of her heart as she handed over the ten duros which were needed to appease her friend's metallic thirst. However, there was nothing else she could do.

Extremely pleased, Doña Cándida went in to see Bringas, who insisted that he felt better, though his head was very weak. The doctor had examined him that morning and took a favourable view of the case, saying that he would probably recover his sight soon. Don Francisco even thought that he could see something when he moved the badage . . . all that was necessary seemed to be rest and patience and taking his medicines regularly.

"Who came in just then?" he asked suddenly.

"I think it's Señor de Torres who has come to ask after you" Cándida replied.

"My head is so weak and in such a state that I thought I heard money being counted. The doctor has told me not to fix my attention on things and I try not to; but I can't help noticing everything that goes on in the house. I simply can't stop doing it; I am always listening. And even when I'm asleep I seem to hear the slightest noise."

Cándida wisely told him that sick brains need rest, and that he ought to try not to think of anything at all but just lie and doze. So long as he was in bed no one ought to talk to him, and the children ought to be kept out of his room. He agreed to everything that she said, and sighed heavily as he added that for him the hardest part of all was trying to repress his desire to know everything that went on in the house and give orders about it.

115

While the two of them were talking in the dim alcove, Rosalía and Torres had been whispering together in the *Saleta*. They took the greatest precautions not to make any noise, but while they were counting out the twenty duros that were in silver, some slight *tin-tin* must have vibrated in the room and the faint waves of sound spread through the apartment until they reached Bringas' ear. Torres was really grieved at his friend's illness, and kept expressing the hope that it was nothing serious. Mompous' book-keeper had had what sounded like a similar attack, he said.

"He was writing one day when suddenly he went blind. He thought at first that it was incurable; but after ten days with his eyes bandaged and a course of medicines, he got all right again, though he has always been a little delicate since. He finished his cure at the Baths at Quinto."

And the good man said goodbye, as much pleased at having got his money as grieved at Don Francisco's misfortune.

Isabelita was sad and nervous and would not eat, so they sent her off to Doña Cándida's rooms to play with Irene and the other children of the quarter, while Alfonsin went to school as usual. But Paquito was so affected by his father's illness that he would not leave the house and could not touch his lunch. Cándida, in fact, was the only person there who ate with her usual appetite.

"You must keep up your strength," she said to Rosalía "and not neglect yourself like that. You must eat properly if you're going to sit up at night and work and attend to everything at the same time ... I don't feel hungry either, but I force myself to eat because I know I should."

Soon after dinner a note arrived from Milagros, saying that everything had been arranged satisfactorily in the end and that she was expecting Rosalía that night. The note breathed happiness and contentment.

"Poor Milagros doesn't know what has happened to us yet" Rosalía said, tearing up the note. "She is urging me to be sure to be there tonight. Go around, my son, and tell her why I can't come; and on your way back stop at Pez's house and tell Carolina too. She is to blame for everything—she and her hairs! What a basilisk of a woman!"

The seamstress came, but Rosalía sent her away again, telling her to come back the following week. In the afternoon Milagros herself appeared, to say how sorry she was not to have heard what had happened sooner, so that she could have flown to her friend to comfort her. Her sincere regret could not entirely hide however the satisfaction she felt over the successful solution of her financial crisis on that critical day. How it had been solved will appear later on.

The Marquesa wanted to know what the doctor had said, and fervently hoped that the blindness was only a matter of a few days. She would pray God to cure Don Francisco, such a good man, the perfect father . . . "But how much I regret that you can't come tonight. It will really be a brilliant affair, and the *buffet* will be magnificent . . . I'll tell you all about it some other time . . . It's a long story."

As she was saying goodbye at the door, she could not restrain the spontaneous expression of her ruling passion. With the manner of one confiding an important secret she told her friend what she was going to wear that night—the white muslin with foulard spots. She had changed the bodice and made a jacket in the style of *Watteau* . . . and at the last moment she had managed to have a *guimpe* made like the one Pilar San Salamo got from Paris . . . She was going to have her hair done high, waved loosely, with a great tress bound round her head, and large curls at the back . . . "But you can't be in the

117

humour for such trifles . . . Goodbye, I'll come in tomorrow to find out how Don Francisco is, and then I'll tell you all about it."

Bringas, who missed nothing that went on in the apartments, said to his wife afterwards:

"I heard you whispering with the Tellería at the door. What has happened? Has some imbecile fallen into the trap after all? Poor woman. Really it's better to eat a piece of bread and an onion, and eat it in peace, than live as those people do in such grandeurs and miseries. And tonight they are having a big party? Really I pity them."

XX

Don Francisco felt much encouraged that afternoon because, when he disobeyed the doctor's orders and lifted the bandage he could see a little, though what he saw was dim and confused and the light hurt his eyes. Still he felt reassured, for it was obvious that his sight was not lost and that he would probably sooner or later recover the use of that most precious of functions. He was much troubled by tickling sensations and also by visions of thousands of shining dots and tiny metallic rays which were constantly shifting and changing—the images that those never to be sufficiently accursed hairs had left on the injured retina.

The poor man bore all these discomforts with resignation, the thing he most minded being that he had to stay in bed. It was torture to him to have to lie still on his back covered with hot sheets. Fortunately after a few days the doctor allowed him to get up on condition that he sat quietly in a chair and did not talk or occupy himself with anything, and also that he kept his eyes rigorously bandaged. So they got him up and installed him in *Gasperini* in a comfortable armchair propped up with pillows. But no one was allowed to visit him, nor would they pay any attention when he begged to have Paquito read the newspapers to him in the evening. But as far as being indifferent to domestic matters went—this was a vain hope. Though he declared that he would leave everything in Rosalía's hands, he could not control his desire to exercise his authority, nor forget what a good use he had made of it during so many years.

119

"Rosalía ..."

"What is it, dear?"

"What are you having for dinner today?"

"Why are you worrying about that?"

"I distinctly smelled beef cooking—don't deny it. It's more important than ever to economize now. You ought to be having potato omelettes, or stuffed artichokes, or sausages, or perhaps, if the doctor orders meat for me, a little roasted veal. And don't forget there's always sheep's head. If you let Cándida do the shopping for you we'll soon find ourselves in the street—just remember that that señora wasted two fortunes on trash. Listen, I want to say something to you. Where is Cándida now?"

"She's in *Furriela*, she can't possibly hear you."

"Why don't you suggest to her—in the nicest possible way of course—that she might go home for her meals now. A guest for a day or two is all right, but we don't want guests perpetually."

"But, my dear, if you only knew how much the poor soul has been helping me! I can't just tell her to go away now."

"What did Prudencia bring from the Plaza de la Cebada?"

"Three bushels of potatoes."

"At how much the bushel?"

"Six reals."

"Listen, my dear, don't forget to put everything down so that I can make up the accounts at the end of the month. And another thing, don't buy any wine, as you know I can't have any. The doctor says I should have half a glass of sherry before meals and Doña Tula promised to send me some, but don't get any if she doesn't. And if Cándida goes on coming in early so that you have to give her her morning chocolate—you're sure no one can hear me?"

"Quite sure."

"Get her the kind they sell at four reals. She will be perfectly satisfied with that. I don't suppose she ever pays more than three for hers. It's the present we'll have to give the doctor I'm worrying about. It's sure to take all our savings. Thank goodness he hasn't called in an oculist: I only hope it won't be necessary. Yesterday he was talking about my going away to some watering place. I can't even bear to think about it. All this nonsense about going to baths is something the doctors have invented to squeeze the last drop out of their patients. In my youth you never heard anything about going to baths, and there was far less illness just because of it— actually fewer people died, I'm sure. If he says anything more about it, frown on the idea, and I will too."

The strangest thing was that even in that miserable condition Bringas would not give up his control of the money for household expenses. While he was in bed he had to let his wife have the keys of the chest in which he kept his money, but as soon as he got up he took over that most important part of household management again. His blindness did not intimidate him, and he used his strong will to conquer his physical weakness. He would get up from his chair and feel his way to the table, open the casket that stood on it and take out the small box in which he kept his money. Even in that short time his sense of touch had acquired the delicacy which those who are deprived of sight possess, and he could tell the coins apart simply by feeling them carefully. With the chest held on his knees, he would take them out one by one and count the required sum into his wife's hand. While he was doing it she would make some timid observation, such as:

"You see, my dear, the expenses are heavier now."

"But they shouldn't be heavier. Economize! Today is Saturday so you'll need the twenty-four reals for the charcoal vendor. Listen, I don't want any more chicken broth unless the Chef sends me up some. Luckily I'm not used to being pampered. The soup from the *cocido*, made with a good marrow bone, is the best soup you can have."

And Rosalía, anxious not to annoy him, agreed with everything he said. After he had taken out the coins needed for the expenses of the day, Bringas would still keep the box on his knees and lifting up its false bottom, take out an old much worn notecase which contained various banknotes. With exquisite delicacy of touch he would unfold these, smooth them out and then carefully fold them up again, saying to himself as he counted them: "This is the one for fifteen hundred, these two are for four thousand," and so forth. He knew them by the order in which they were arranged. After he had counted the bills he would put everything back in the casket again, lock it and put the key in the left hand pocket of his house coat, and then would let his wife guide him back to his armchair. This performance always took place behind locked doors, for Bringas always sent Rosalía to shoot the bolt before taking out his treasure.

A week had passed since St. Anthony's day—a very sad date in that house—and still the invalid had not made much progress. But if he was no better, at any rate he was no worse, which is always some consolation in cases of illness. There was no doubt that the optic nerve still functioned and that Don Francisco could see. But if he lifted the bandage even for an instant, the light in his eyes was so acutely painful that he had to put it back immediately. His wife looked after him with the greatest skill and devotion, putting compresses of belladonna on his eyelids when he was in pain and rubbing his temples with belladonna and laudanum. But her chief care was trying to keep the bandage in place, for Don Francisco was so energetic that as soon as he felt even a little better he would slip it up and have a look around.

"For God's sake," Rosalía would exclaim. "Don't do that . . . You will only make yourself worse. You are like a child. The doctor tells you on no account to take the bandage off and you keep on doing it. You'll never get well like that. If you'll only have patience, you'll be able to take it off one day and stare right into the sun. But now you must stay blind, blind, nothing but blind . . . and if you insist on 'opening the window' as you call it, I'll tie your hands like a baby's."

"This cursed bandage weighs on me like a stone wall," Bringas would say with a sigh. "It's true that it's very painful when I look at the light, but always being in darkness makes me feel so wretched. It's a comfort to see something sometimes, even if it's only a room with the objects in it, confused and as if they were half rubbed out. And it's a consolation to see you—and if this injured retina isn't deceiving me you've got on a silk dress . . . Is it the one Augustin gave you? I thought you had cut that one up to make a dress for Isabelita . . . Anyway, it can't be that one, because the one you're wearing is red."

XXI

Rosalía was standing some distance from him near the door. For a moment she was extremely disconcerted, but she promptly recovered herself and said, laughing:

"So I'm wearing a silk dress, am I? A fine occasion for silk dresses, I must say! There, you see .what happens when you 'open the window'. You see everything distorted, wool turns into silk and this dull dirty brown becomes a beautiful red."

"But I swear to you—"

"Don't swear—it's a sin . . . a silk dress—I only wish it were!"

And she left the room quickly and went to the *Camón*; there she hurriedly changed the dress she had on for the old one which she usually wore around the house and returned very quietly to *Gasperini*.

"Are you there?" Bringas enquired after waiting for some moments during which he must have doubted whether his wife were there or not.

"Yes, I am here," Rosalía replied promptly. "The baker came. Today I've only taken three pounds of bread."

"But I could swear—do I really see everything transformed like that?"

"Still talking about the dress?" Rosalía said, coming to him and caressing his cheek.

The blind man touched the cloth of her dress and ran it between his fingers, murmuring:

"To the touch it certainly is wool, and very good wool too—"

Then after a pause during which his wife did not speak, he went on:

"That is, if you didn't change it during those few moments when you were out of the room—I seemed to hear a rustling of cloth . . ."

"Jesus! What ears you have! But you well may have heard cloth rustling, because the dressmaker is here working on those dresses of Milagros'."

Paquito came in just then and sat down by his father to amuse him with anecdotes he'd heard that day and passages read from the newspapers. Milagros came in later in the afternoon as she had been doing every day showing a truly sisterly concern for Don Francisco's health. She stayed with him for a while and then went off with her colleague to the most distant room in the apartment, which was *Furriela*.

She had never really explained to her friend how she had managed to get out of that impasse on the 14th; but it must have been by means of an extremely short term loan to judge by later events. What is certain is that the supper was a splendid affair and that a celebrated salon chronicler, writing in that emasculated style which is peculiar to them, praised it to the skies, making use of phrases something between French and Spanish which I shall not reproduce here for fear of making my readers sick. When they read it to Don Francisco he could only say:

"Who can have been such an imbecile?"

For a few days after the soirée Milagros seemed very contented, but little by little this contentment decreased, and by the twentieth of the month she had begun to have sudden fits of depression, while by St. John's Day her periods of tranquillity had become shorter than those of distress, and she confided some very disagreeable possibilities to her friend. Rosalía heard her with alarm, for she saw that the cloud that was approaching was blacker than the one that had passed. Meanwhile the Marquesa gave her friend such extravagant proofs of affection that she hardly knew how to thank her enough. In the early days of her husband's illness Rosalía had almost entirely lost her interest in clothes. But after the doctor announced that Don Francisco would probably soon be well again her passion for dress and elegance resumed its sway, so that the presents which Milagros gave her at this melancholy period of her life went straight to her soul. And they were not trifles, these presents! One afternoon as she was leaving, the Marquesa said:

"Do you know, I don't think my *Florian* hat really suits me. But it would be perfect on *you*—I'll send it to you."

And she did. Another day when they were talking about dresses for cooler weather, she said:

"I don't really like that mohair dress I'm having made. I'll send it to you. You'll be going to some watering place soon with your husband, and it will come in useful for that. No, don't thank me for it, it's no use to me. And I'll bring that *fichu* with the green ribbons and that felt shape I have, so that you can trim yourself a hat. It will be perfect for the baths. I'll send along some flowers and aigrettes for it at the same time—I must have six boxes of things of that sort at home. And another thing— the dressmaker brought back my red dress today, but I don't think it's becoming at all. That colour only suits plump fair women with really fresh faces. Would you like it? You could probably let it out to fit you—anyway the material is handsome."

At the period when these fine clothes were coming into the apartment, Rosalía was still almost indifferent to such things and stored them all away in *Camón*. But sometimes when she was in better spirits because the doctor was particularly encouraging, she would shut herself up there and try them on, till, finally unable to resist the temptation, she got Emilia in to alter them. Occasionally she would even let herself be carried away by enthusiasm and put on the red dress and the *Florian* hat and come out of *Camón* and take a few turns around the apartment in them. But to do this she had to wait until the servants and the children were out and Don Francisco was shut up in *Gasperini* with Paquito. Sometimes she showed herself to Cándida, but the old lady was always taken with such a fury of applause that she had to appear with a finger on her lips, for her husband's subtle ear could perceive anything that happened even far away in the *Saleta*. Her gay moods would not last long however, and she would soon return to her secret chamber and take off her handsome clothes, saying to herself with a sigh:

"I don't seem to care about anything now; I haven't the spirit for these jokes any longer."

By the 26th the Marquesa could no longer contain the sadness that filled her breast and poured it out to her friend, saying as a preface to this pathetic exhortation:

"I'll send you the muslin dress with the violet spots too, and my *valenciennes* and *Alençon* lace and the *guipure* as well—what use is anything to me now? The few jewels I have left shall be yours too some day, for there is nothing left for me but to enter a convent or run away.— Oh, if God would take me to himself, what a service he would be doing me! But I hardly know what I am saying any longer. You are frightened at seeing me so distressed, but if you only knew! Calamities rain down on me as if the Lord wanted to try me. They say that you acquire merits for eternal life in that way, and it should be so, for if it isn't what a sad thing life is! I must have been born under an evil star! Up to now I've always managed to get out of the difficulties my *mariducho* gets me into. God knows what efforts, I might say what heroic efforts,

I've made in the last few years, what struggles I've had
trying to keep up the dignity of the house so that the
children shouldn't lack for anything. There have been
days when I was afraid the servants wouldn't even be
able to announce that the soup was on the table. And what
humiliations I've suffered in these unending struggles with
creditors, with vulgar people and every sort of rogue!
But when your difficulties go on accumulating, and you
keep up the system of opening one hole to close another
too long, a day arrives when the whole thing comes
down on you at once. It's like being in a very old ship
that has been mended over and over—Suddenly, the sides
open ..."

By the time she had reached the image of the sinking
ship the poor lady's language was not so much speech
as one continual sob. Rosalía was almost as upset as she
was, and begged her to explain the cause of her trouble:
together they might think of some solution. But the
Marquesa could not (or perhaps would not) expound her
difficulty in categorical terms. She would only say that
it was a matter of having to be ready with a large sum of
money by the end of the month, and that if she did not
have it she would be in the most serious difficulty she
had ever been in, and would possibly, or rather certainly,
be disgraced by being brought into court. But what *was*
the trouble, Rosalía insisted, had some friend compromised himself to get her out of her difficulty, or had
she put her signature to some paper? Foolish creature, it
would have been better to cut off her hand first—though
it's true that if she had cut off her hand there wouldn't
have been any supper on that cursed night of the 14th.

Rosalía asked why Milagros didn't write to her
administrator in Almendralejo and get him to anticipate
the quarterly rents, even if it had to be done at a discount.
Milagros answered with a sigh that she had already done

it, but that even so she could not count on receiving the money before the 15th of July. The only comfort was that the rents were certain to be paid and that the person who was going to advance the money would pay it punctually on the agreed date.

"But couldn't you come to some arrangement with your creditors then?"

"Oh, impossible, my dear, impossible—as impossible as that bulls should fly or that my husband should show any signs of commonsense."

"What about your sister?"

"Oh, that's even more impossible."

Rosalía shrugged her shoulders; she could not think of anything else. But Milagros startled her out of her profound depression by throwing her arms around her neck and whispering in her ear:

"You . . . you . . . friend of my soul . . . You can save me . . ."

After she had said it she fell into a sort of convulsive fit—what women call an attack of nerves, since they have to call it something—and this was followed by one of those spasms which go by the attractive name of syncope.

XXII

It was necessary to bring the Marquesa a glass of water
and unhook her corset and do all sorts of other things
to bring her round.

"But how can *I* help you?" Rosalía demanded in a tone
of alarm after the Marquesa had come to herself again.
"What can I do?"

"You could ask Don Francisco to give me the money.
I would pay him interest of course and give him a properly made out agreement. I would show him my
administrator's letter, in which he says that I shall certainly
have the money by the 15th of July. And my administrator isn't a phantom like Doña Cándida's, but a man of
flesh and blood. You can tell that by the twenty per cent
it costs you when he anticipates the rents!"

Rosalía made every sign of refusal she could think of
both with head and voice.

"My dear, you are under an illusion. My husband
hasn't got a penny, and if he had he wouldn't give it
to you. You don't know him."

To these decided negatives the agonized woman opposed
reasons which showed both her perspicuity and the infinite
resources of her talent. She was perfectly certain that Don
Francisco had the money. That point once decided, the problem reduced itself into how the mysterious treasure could be
transferred from his coffers to the needy hands of Milagros.
If the faithful wife should take it upon herself to make this
loan (and, after all, the hoard was not a Church treasure) she
could easily do it without her husband's ever even knowing
about it; because the money could certainly be put back again
before he was in a condition to notice that it wasn't there.

"Surely you don't think that Don Francisco is going to get his sight back before the 15th of July!"

This remark, which Milagros made quite unthinkingly in the heat of improvisation, wounded Rosalía to the quick.

"I hope he will," she said. "And even if he isn't going to, I don't want to even think of it's being such a long time before he recovers his sight."

"You must forgive me, my dear, for being so thoughtless; sometimes one says such foolish things. But you don't know how we burn and twist and even blaspheme, we damned souls in this hell of a Madrid. The things I think of sometimes! Don't be alarmed, but believe me I really mean it: at moments like this I would be quite capable of robbing someone—with the intention of returning the money of course. Sometimes when I go home and see the porter in his basement room, eating garlic soup with his wife, I really envy them. I'd like to send them upstairs and take their place below, even if I had to sweep the doorway and polish the brass and wash the staircase from top to bottom. As I told you before, I would be only too glad to shut myself up in a convent and forget the world. But my children, my poor children— what would become of them if I did? Still, when I've found a good husband for Maria, who knows? I might decide to seek peace in the religious life. At any rate I shall renounce the world then and live shut up in my own house, and always wear a Carmelite habit. In the morning I'd go to mass, and in the afternoon visit some friend, and in the evening, home and early to bed—it's the healthiest thing anyway. Ah, what a happy life that would be!"

After reverting to her previous suggestions about money, and only obtaining chilly negatives from Rosalía, she remarked suddenly:

"Let's see if we can't go to the baths together—only I'd have to make it rather late, I couldn't manage it before the beginning of August. Hasn't the doctor said what waters would be best for Bringas yet? Not that it matters to me. For the kind of ailments I have, one water is as good as another; the benefit lies in moving about and getting out of this oven for a while."

On the subject of watering places Rosalía was much more communicative than on the question of a loan; she said that she was very anxious to go away somewhere, but that so far the doctor hadn't made any pronouncement. Bringas was most unwilling to go because of the expense; but if the doctor ordered it he could hardly refuse, could he? She would certainly be the better of a change and some diversion, for she felt very tired and run down. From the discussion of watering places they passed easily to the subject of clothes, and from talking about dresses to trying them on. Rosalía put on the lawn, which was nearly finished; and her friend congratulated her so warmly on her appearance in it that the daughter of the Pipaóns nearly burst with pride.

"But you are so elegant! Whatever you wear looks marvellous on you! It's the truth. I don't say it just to please you—I say the same thing to everyone. You've got such a figure, and such wonderful shoulders! If you wanted to take the trouble and make an effort over your clothes, no one could hold a candle to you!"

It is unnecessary to say how Rosalía was affected by this praise. How stupid it was that a person with such natural advantages should have to hide her best clothes and invent a thousand stories to explain her possession of these lovely garments, which seemed to have been fitted on her beautiful body by the Angels of Fashion! While she was taking off the lawn dress, she kept brooding over the tremendous problem of explaining to her husband how she had got them, for when he recovered his sight, she must either explain them or not wear them at all.

Before Milagros took leave of her friend, she repeated her tale of woes and hinted once more at the remedy she had discovered for them. In the end, simply with the idea of comforting her, Rosalía murmured *We'll see*; and the Tellería's face was illumined with a ray of hope.

"Tomorrow," she said, when they were already standing in the doorway, "tomorrow, I'll send you that *blonde* you liked so much. No, don't thank me. If you get me out of this hole, I'll owe you eternal gratitude."

And she gave her friend two resounding kisses.

It was at just about this time that Don Manuel Pez returned from Archena, well pleased with the effect of the waters, for he had a good colour and appetite and was in excellent spirits. The first visit he paid was to Bringas, for he had heard of his friend's illness while he was still away at the baths; and he did all he could to cheer him up, declaring that he meant to come to see him morning, noon and night—in fact to spend all his free time with him. And he fulfilled this promise to the letter, until his presence in the house became so taken for granted that it almost seemed that something was missing when he was not there. Sometimes he would entertain the invalid by chatting about the political events of the time and repeating the current rumours; but he always had to take care not to talk of danger to the throne or of things being in a bad way. For as soon as anyone spoke of the *so-called* revolution, Don Francisco became perfectly wretched and began to sigh as if his heart would break.

When Bringas had other visitors or they thought that he had been talking too much, Pez would leave *Gasperini* and go to one of the other rooms to find Rosalía, and she would be much struck by his manner on these occasions. It would always be quiet and respectful, and his gallantries were discreet and well-bred. She responded to this attitude towards her with an admiration of the most complete

133

purity. Every day he assumed greater proportions in her mind as the perfect type of the higher civil servant, courteous and proud. The ideal man, for this descendant of the Pipaóns, could only have been one with the golden atmosphere of a government appointment around him. If Pez had not been a civil servant, he would have lost a great deal in her eyes. She was so accustomed to thinking of the world as a huge office that she could hardly envisage any other means of making a livelihood except by having a post at court or in the Civil Service. And then there was that elegant air of Pez's, that black frock coat that never had a stain, those high collars that were whiter than the driven snow, those hands that were so smooth and carefully tended!

XXIII

The very way Pez had of brushing his hair was distinguished; at once so simple and so well-bred, like his discreet use of fine perfumes and the scent that rose from his odorous Russian leather card-case. When he talked to Rosalía he managed to employ some ingenious *double entendre* in everything he said; and she would perhaps not have been too well pleased by this if she had not felt that she deserved every word of it and that society had certain debts of homage to her which had never been paid; so that Pez came to be for her the one who in the name of society was rendering those neglected tributes.

The Bringas' apartment was terrribly hot in the afternoon when the rooms caught the western sun, and the family generally sought relief at that time by going out on the terrace. One afternoon Don Francisco accompanied them, after getting the doctor's permission, and took a couple of turns leaning on Pez's arm; but he did not really feel up to it and decided to leave such expeditions until he was better. However he did not want any of the family to give up this diversion on his account, and often urged his wife to go out and get some fresh air, saying to her:

"My dear, it distresses me to see you shut up in this frying-pan all day. I don't really feel the heat because I'm sitting still. But you are running about all the time; you must be burning up with the heat. Do go out for a bit."

Rosalía would generally refuse; but on some afternoons she would go out on the terrace for a while, and Pez always kept her company on such occasions. There was one afternoon when Pez had gone out early alone, for the rooms had become really insufferable. After a time he was joined by Rosalía, dressed in her crimson silk and fanning herself gracefully. She looked extremely elegant, though the style of her costume was rather extravagant, as Milagros had remarked. Still, she was handsome, remarkably handsome, and if I counted the bouquets that Pez tossed to her I would turn this book into a long madrigal. Without quite knowing how it came about, Rosalía gave rein to a sudden violent impulse which bubbled up within her and told her friend about the occasion on which her husband had lifted up his bandage unexpectedly and surprised her in the crimson dress.

"Poor soul," she said. "He doesn't like to see me too well dressed—perhaps he is right."

From telling this story she went on to a general account of her difficulties. Bringas thought that you should only have a few clothes and look after them carefully; and that the metamorphoses of a single garment could go on forever. She really hardly knows what to do sometimes. She realised that she ought to obey her husband, and yet she wanted to look well for his sake. "If it were only for myself, I wouldn't mind so much, but I do it for him; so that people won't say that they've seen me going around looking like a scarecrow."

Pez agreed vehemently with everything she said and became indignant against his friend for this penuriousness, which was so contrary to the social exigencies. "He doesn't seem to realize that his own dignity, his own appearance, his own best interest ... How can such a man make a career for himself—a man who thinks like that, a man who acts in that way?"

Rosalía became still more expansive in his sympathetic warmth, and did not conceal the agonies she suffered in

trying to hide the small purchases she was obliged to make from time to time.

"You don't know what I suffer sometimes. I have to lie, to make up all sorts of stories."

Pez showed himself a man of such noble inclinations, that, after he had condoled with his friend feelingly, he offered to lend her his entirely disinterested aid if she should find herself in difficulties owing to Bringas' miserly habits.

"Either we are friends, or we are not; either we're frank with each other, or we are not; it would be entirely a matter between the two of us, no one else would ever know. How could I bear to see you, with your splendid appearance, your unequalled figure, not shown in your true lustre—"

And this speech was followed by such a deluge of compliments that Rosalía fanned herself to cool the vivid warmth that flushed her face, while the nostrils of her pretty nose grew more and more inflated.

"I must take him his cooling drink, it's seven o'clock," she said suddenly.

She needed one quite as much herself.

The doctor was so encouraging the next day that laughter was heard once more in the apartment, and the patient himself recovered his good spirits and was full of impatience and vivacity.

"Next week," the doctor said, "we'll take off the bandage, and by the week after that you should be able to see almost perfectly and even go out in the streets with dark glasses on. If you are careful not to do any work that tires the eyes this summer and autumn, you ought to be able to go back to the office and resume your ordinary occupations—so long, that is, as you don't start playing with hairs again! Mechanical tasks, on the other hand, occupations in which you use your muscles

139

would be good for you; carpentry for instance, or gardening. But you mustn't take up anything that requires close attention."

Bringas was far from pleased, however, when the old man suggested that he should finish his cure by taking the waters at Cestona. There was a good deal of "Nonsense. In the old days nobody went to baths and fewer people died" at that point in the conversation; as well as "The baths are only a pretext for spending money and giving women an excuse for showing off their clothes." To all this the aged Galen replied with a vehement defence of the virtues of medicinal waters.

"Say what you will, my dear," Rosalía declared, after the old gentleman had gone; and there was even more eloquence in her nostrils than on her lips. "The doctor has ordered you to go to Cestona, and that's all there is to it! You can't decide such things for yourself. In a case like this you must do everything you're told to, so that if you should get worse again, you'd have no cause for regrets. Besides, the climate of the provinces is bracing in summer and that will shorten your convalescence. As far as I'm concerned, I'd just as soon stay here— travelling is always more of a nuisance than a pleasure; but the children really ought not to pass another year without having some sea bathing."

In spite of the prospect of the journey with all its attendant annoyances, such as spending too much money, having to beg for free tickets and other anxieties, Don Francisco was so pleased to be better that his happiness rose to his lips and he could not be silent for a moment.

"As soon as I'm well, my dear, I'm going to start my carpentry. I'm going to make you a wardrobe for your clothes—such a mangificent wardrobe that it will be famous and people will take tickets to see it as they do for the Natural History Museum and the Armoury! The man who leases the right to cut timber at Balsain has offered me as much pinewood as I need at any time. And there's a deposit of mahogany in the attics above us that's simply rotting away—Her Majesty would certainly let me have some. Then the contractor, who is making the pantheon of the Infantes at the Escorial, has offered to give me all the marble I want. I'll tell you what I'll do, I'll make you a marble wardrobe, a pantheon for your dresses! No, perhaps it would be too heavy; I'll use the marble to make a magnificent wash-table and console. And I'll make something for Cándida too. I'm fairly well off for tools fortunately; but I'll buy some more, or perhaps the contractor who is doing the work at la Granja would lend me some."

At this point the widow of Garcia Grande had to put in her oar, telling the artist that she could lend him the most sumptuous and elegant models to copy. She had an inlaid console table which had once belonged to Grimaldi himself and a wardrobe which had been brought from Paris by Madame des Ursins. While as to the workshop that Don Francisco would need for all these tasks, Her Majesty would certainly let him use one of the uninhabited rooms on the Third Floor. Just next door to her there was one that had an excellent light; it had once been used as a dovecote but was now empty and couldn't be more suitable for his work if it had been made especially for the purpose.

Bringas rubbed his hands together when he heard this with such enthusiasm that sparks almost flew from them.

"Splendid, splendid. Once I can use my eyes, you'll see what I shall do."

It is unnecessary to say that Rosalía was happy too. Her dear husband would recover his health and his sight and would again fill his role of paternal sovereign in the house. But, as good fortune is never perfect in this detestable world and happy events always have a sad penumbra around them, Rosalía's pleasure had an uncomfortable dark side. It was produced by the memory of those pawned candlesticks and the thought of the absolute necessity of redeeming them before her husband recovered his sight and with it his vigilant watchfulness and that implacable curiosity. One thing was certain; if the happy day of recovered vision arrived and the candlesticks were not on the console table and the earrings not in the lady's charming ears, their absence would be the first thing that the household lynx would notice. It horrified her to think of it; and in spite of her gladness she was in a state of half painful perplexity. Her condition could be best described by saying that sometimes she would have been glad not to be so happy.

The impatience and excitement that Bringas felt manifested itself in a perfect fever of domestic intervention —a delirium of household management. He tried to watch over and direct everything as if he could see, and never stopped making suggestions and then answering the questions that he had raised himself until his wife was almost driven crazy with his fussing.

XXIV

"My dear, listen. If we do have to go to those wretched baths, you must manage to get along with the dresses you have. Change them, alter them, take something off one and put it on another; they will look like new—everyone will think you got your clothes from Worth. You know even Duchesses do these things. I am counting on Her Majesty to give me a letter to the Chief of Transport to let me have free tickets for all of us. There's another thing that you could manage if you took it in hand properly; you could get La Señora to make the treasury pay my salary twice for July. It's all a matter of knowing how to do these things. When you are telling her about our trip, look depressed, and say that we may not be able to go because—. It depends on catching Her Majesty in a generous mood and that should be easy because she almost always is in one. I leave it to you.

"The children won't need any clothes—perhaps some little hats. But don't get them anything until I can see what you are getting; you might dress them up too much. I'll wear the panama hat Augustin left behind, and with my light wool overcoat I got six years ago and my nankeen suit which always looks like new, I'll be ready for anything. We must try to make them give us a reserved carriage so that we can take our food with us and a little stove to make chocolate on and a mattress and pillows, and all the other things we'll need. Well, we'll manage it somehow."

But the lecture went on:

"What was that noise I heard just then? What are they breaking now, for heaven's sake? Since I've been sitting here unable to see, I've heard at least a dozen things broken. When I can see again I'm going to find the place a perfect ruin! And I can't understand this enormous comsumption of petroleum and soap, now that I don't need a light and don't change my clothes so often or wear collars and cuffs. And this twenty four reals for lemons! Have they brought the orchards of Valencia to us? If we had to pay for my medicines too, we'd soon be begging for alms. Well, when I recover, everything will be all right again—it seems to me that since I've been like this no one pays any attention to what I say. *When the master can't see!* I notice you don't get the cheaper cuts of meat any more, and you seem to have forgotten all about dried cod, which is excellent when it is properly cooked. You say that you can't attend to everything— but why can't Paquito polish the knives and forks when he comes back from his classes? I suppose a gentleman law student thinks himself demeaned by performing such tasks.—Well, all I can say is that his father has done it often enough and will do it again when he gets his sight back. Another thing—I'm sure you don't take the children's shoes off when they come back from school and put on their old ones; I can tell by the noise they make when they are running around that they still have their street shoes on. You really might have thought of getting them some rope soled sandals; they are much the best thing for this weather. But I shall get my sight back soon, I hope, and then everything will return to that economical routine which is the only way in which we can afford to live."

This irksome refrain had never sounded very pleasantly in Rosalía's ears, and she liked it less than ever now. However, she tried to get everything back into its accustomed train, and to obey the innumerable rules and regulations which flowed unceasingly from the inexhaustible source of domestic legislation. She got rope-soled sandals for the children; and Bringas decided that they shouldn't go to school during the middle of the summer because the excessive heat was bad for them, and idleness, besides being an economy, was hygenic. They were only too pleased, and spent the whole day playing in the corridors dressed in loose clothes made of cotton drill, or else went up to the Third Floor to join Irene and the other children who lived there in their games. They were the happiest beings in the whole great building, almost as happy as the doves that nest in the niches and enfold the huge edifice in an atmosphere of cooing.

At about that time the Bringas family received a visit which caused Don Francisco and his wife more surprise than pleasure; it was from a person whose name they hardly liked to remember, Refugio Sánchez Emperador (disreputable sister of that snake in the grass, Amparo—the Cinderella, poor relation and household drudge—who had so nearly made a matrimonial prize of their rich and generous cousin Augustin Caballero, and, even after the marriage had been broken off owing to his discovery of an unfortunate incident in her past, had shamelessly gone off with him, unmarried, to Bordeaux). Refugio presented herself at the door one day, as we have said, and behaved in such a humble way that Rosalía thought she must be dissembling her natural insolence so as to be able to mix with decent people, if only for an hour or two.

She soon explained the motive of her visit. Her sister had written her from Burgos; she was so distressed to hear of Don Francisco's illness. Since she had heard of it, she said, she could think of nothing else and she asked Refugio to go around immediately, find out how Don Francisco was and write to her by return of post; and also to keep her informed of his state and send her news of him two or three times a week. Don Augustin,

Amparo wrote, was as distressed as she was and just as anxious to get news.

Bringas expressed his gratitude for their solicitude warmly; but said so much about the improvement in his state that Refugio might well have thought that he only wore that enormous bandage as a caprice. "Tell them that I am really getting on well now and that I thank them very much indeed for being so attentive."

Rosalía felt a strong desire to say a few well chosen words to this creature who had had the impertinence to profane their honourable house by entering it, but Don Francisco's composure, as well as the girl's polite behaviour, made her restrain herself. However she could not bring herself to keep up the usual social formulas, and hardly greeted the visitor, not even shaking hands with her, and, while the girl was talking to Bringas kept coming and going about the house as if no one were there. As she passed to and fro however she could not help noticing something which much diminished her antipathy. It was not Refugio's polite manner and quiet behaviour, nor the reasonable and sensible things that she was saying; it was her costume. This was really elegant, made in the latest style, and admirably fitted and trimmed. Rosalía looked at her obliquely, wondering where she had got the fine woollen material her dress was made of; it was such an unusual and charming shade. And she kept observing her appearance with surprise, for she looked so neat and was wearing such handsome gloves and such pretty, new shoes. She really is most attractive, Rosalía thought to herself, wishing that she could ask where she got the material of her dress—but probably Amparo had sent it to her from Bordeaux.

"And what are you doing with yourself now?" Don Francisco asked, turning his face towards his visitor as if he could see her through the bandage.

"I?" the Señorita de Sánchez exclaimed, looking a little disconcerted by the question, but quickly recovering herself. "Nothing much. I don't work any more. My health is delicate; sometimes I have difficulty in breathing and pass several nights in succession without sleeping. When I go to bed it seems as if I had a stone here—. My sister sends me enough to live on comfortably without working. I live with some very respectable ladies who are extremely kind to me—I like a quiet life. But, I was going to tell you, my sister thinks I ought to have something to do, so as I can't sew, she suggested that I might set up as a dealer in articles of luxury. She has sent me a huge box of hats and *fichus* and shawls, bows and cravats and *guimpes*. They are the most charming things, nothin like them has ever been seen in Madrid before, they are so new and in such good taste. And she has sent hat shapes of straw and felt as well, and ribbons of every imaginable kind, and feathers and marabouts and aigrettes and plumes—in fact everything you can think of. I am trying to show it all as well as I can, and I've already found some customers among the nobility. A good many ladies have come to see my things and all of them have been simply enchanted. I've had some cards printed."

Here she took a card out of her purse and gave it to Rosalía, who, though still half frowning, deigned to reward the young woman with a benevolent smile, the first she had received from those disdainful lips. And, so long as the girl talked about the charming articles with which she was setting up in business, Rosalía listened to her with interest, pardoning perhaps the vileness of the speaker for the sake of the exalted nature of the goods in which she trafficked.

"So you're going in for fashions?" Don Francisco said, rubbing his hands. "An excellent business, I must say. Think of all the tricks your clients will be up to! In

Madrid the desire for luxury is in exactly inverse relation to the means to pay for it, so look out, my dear. If your sister didn't send you something to live on, you'd soon find yourself in the streets, with what you'll make on articles of luxury. And now you've come to flatter us into being customers—Child, for heaven's sake, knock at some other door! Your industry is the ruin of families and the noviciate for the poorhouse. But I wish you luck all the same. And I advise you strongly to show your customers no mercy. If you want to make a living, be hard on them; if a thing is worth twelve duros, ask forty, and overcharge the ones who do pay to make up for all the ones from whom you'll never get a penny."

He laughed heartily and the two women laughed with him. And the lady of the house not only laughed, but, most surprisingly, accompanied Refugio to the door and said goodbye amiably.

"You didn't ask her whether they had got married, I suppose?" she enquired when she had returned to *Gasperini.*

"I had the question on the tip of my tongue more than once," he answered, "but I didn't ask it, because I was afraid that if she said *No,* it would annoy me so much that it would be bad for my eyes."

"It was all I could do not to turn her out of the house," the lady declared, her face expressing that righteous anger which is the legitimate child of a feeling of self-respect. "It's outrageous that she should come here with messages from that fine sister of hers—another one just like her! As if we cared whether Amparo was thinking of us or not! And I don't care about Augustin's feelings either. People like that think no more of the Catechism than of a page of Hallelujahs. I don't know how you had the patience to sit and listen to all those lies and nonsense. And now she's going to go in for fashionable accessories! What trash they will be—I don't even want to think about them!"

But the entrance of Señor de Pez put an end to the series of observations which would probably have illustrated this subject.

It was soon after this visit that Bringas, who never tired of giving orders, decided that until the weather got cooler they would have dinner at half past one and supper at nine in the traditional Spanish way. This was not only more convenient in hot weather but more economical, for there was a distinct saving in charcoal. Supper, he decided, should be something light, for instance lentils and a thin soup of spinach and beans, or else garlic soup, and there would be no meat course at night. The only trouble about this arrangement was that the two meals were so far apart that the family got hungry in between and had to have chocolate during the afternoon. This would have been an unbearable expense, since Doña Cándida had attached herself to the family as closely as a spray of goosegrass and was always there at chocolate time, if Heaven had not come to Don Francisco's aid in the shape of Doña Tula. She had adopted the same summer meal hours and served chocolate during the afternoon for her household and for any visitors who cared to drop in; and she almost always sent the invalid a pot of it (it was a particularly rich chocolate) well flanked with sponge fingers.

"Doña Tula is so attentive," Bringas used to say appreciatively, when he heard his neighbour's maid coming in again with the tray.

Rosalía often went to the Condesa's rooms for these afternoon gatherings, where Pez rarely failed to put in an appearance, and there were other regular visitors from among the highly-placed personnel in the Palace-city; for instance the Intendant's sister, and one of the chaplains,

149

the Second Chamberlain and the Inspector General, the doctor and various others. Milagros, however, was never there; she did not come to her sister's apartments any more; they had been on bad terms for a long time. But Maria was always present, and the visitors were all enchanted by her and inclined to spoil her. The Señora de Bringas displayed her Indian lawn in public, and Cándida appeared in her black grosgrain, the only dress she possessed that was still fit to wear.

It is hardly necessary to state that when Pez was present he out-talked everyone, either on politics or on any other weighty subject. But I must confess for my part that his measured way of speaking had some narcotic effect upon me. As soon as he began to explain his reasons for being on terms with the moderate party, a delightful drowsiness began to steal over me as if I had taken a draught of henbane; and Doña Tula's easy chair, caressing me in its warm arms, invited me to sleep. Nevertheless, courtesy impelled me to resist this inclination, and the two impulses struggling within me produced a state of what doctors call *waking coma*—a seeing without seeing, a hearing without hearing, the image turning into the dream, the sounds growing confused and far away. Also I must admit that there were other agents of lethargy working upon my brain; such as the picturesque room, half shuttered because of the heat, the light that filtered through the awnings and gave a tropical colouring to their enormous flowers, the low tone of the faded carpet—the tone of everything in that drowsy place—Doña Cándida's slight clearing of the throat and the yawns she discreetly covered with her hand, the beauty of Maria Sudre, which in that light seemed to be something not of this world, Rosalía's lawn dress with its tiny spots that dazzled the eyes, and finally the lullaby sound of the rocking chairs, and the fluttering of the fans of the five or six ladies who were sitting in them. As the sticks of the fans glittered, so the phrases flashed out one after another—The summer has come early this year and is going to be cruel . . . The Generals have reached the Canaries . . . Prim is in Vichy . . . The Queen is going to La Granja and afterwards to Lequito . . . Trains are being worn shorter now, and they aren't being worn at all at watering places . . . Gonzalez Bravo has a stomach-ache . . . Cabrera has been to see the *Niño tirso* . . .

Finally the voice of Pez detached itself from the others (its tone seemed somehow to be influenced by his golden artificial-looking moustache) and the narcotic influence increased. He could not observe without bitter sadness, it seemed, the state to which things had come and for which certain people were responsible. The revolution with its *all or nothing*, and the moderates with their *laisser faire* policy, were bringing the country to the edge of a precipice, to the edge of an abyss. You could never have progress like that, nor improvements, nor even administration. He was always saying: 'We must have more administration', but it was preaching in the desert. All the public services had gone to the dogs. He himself had an ideal which he always kept in front of him—but how could it be realised? His ideal was the perfect administrative system, with eighty or ninety ministries. There should be no manifestation of the national life which escaped the wise tutelage of the State. The State must work and think for the country, because only the State is intelligent. Knowing that it was impossible to realise this ideal, he had retired into his own sad thoughts and affected that sovereign indifference to everything round him which they observed. He considered himself superior to his contemporaries because at least he saw more clearly than they did and could imagine something better; and he consoled himself by holding fast to his principles in the midst of the general rot. His clean conscience was his reward. He hoped to God that he would never lose this ideal; he hoped ...

I don't know how much time elapsed between Pez's second *hoped* and a discreet tap which Doña Cándida gave me on the knee.

"You are absent-minded," she said.

"No, no, Señora, not at all. I was following what Don Manuel Pez said closely—he was saying—"

"But Don Manuel went out on the terrace long ago. It is Serafinita de Lantigua who is talking now. She is telling us about the death of her husband. I am horrified—"

"So am I ... horrified ..."

XXV

They were strolling indolently about on the terrace as if they were the makers of time, Pez and Rosalía and the sister of the Intendant. But the latter presently went into the Lord Chamberlain's apartments, and the elegant pair were left alone together. Poor Don Manuel was really much to be pitied at this time, for his wife's religious monomania had reached such a pitch that it had become quite insupportable.

"You can't imagine how it maddened me," Pez complained, "having to sit there and listen to Serafinita telling that old story about her sufferings for the thousandth time. I wanted to bolt when she began. That voice of hers with its tone like a choir chanting and those funereal sighs she gives get on my nerves to such a point—. I am a religious man; I believe whatever the Church tells me to believe—but those people who *go to bed with God and get up with God* really nauseate me. And it's that Serafinita who's to blame for my poor Carolina's losing her wits; she's the author of all my misfortune and of this hatred I feel for my home. My friend, you don't know how dreadful it is to have a horror of your own home; you are lucky not to know. I only want to stay out all day now and never go back at all. Insensibly I'm beginning to think of my friend's house as my own, because there is no comparison between the cordial warmth I find here and the dry coldness that meets me there. I'm a man who can't live without affection; it's as necessary to me as the air I breathe, without it I feel asphyxiated, I die. And wherever I find this warmth of affection there I set up my tent."

Just then Isabelita and Alfonsin came running by. They were out of breath and perspiring freely from playing with Irene and the Chef's little girls in the galleries on the Third Floor.

"But, child, what a state you're in!" Rosalía exclaimed, catching the little girl as she went by. "Your face is as red as a lobster. There's a breeze here; go inside quickly or you'll catch cold. And look at this little wretch, what a state he's in—as naked as Adam! Look at those knees! If you made his clothes of iron, it would be just the same."

"He's a perfect imp; he'll be a real man one day," Pez said, kissing the little boy and then kissing his sister too.

"Give me a penny!" the urchin demanded impudently.

"See what a horror he is! Child, what are you thinking of asking for pennies like that? Don't pay any attention to him, please, Don Manuel. He has picked up this bad habit of asking everyone he meets for pennies; I can't think where he got it. I couldn't help laughing the other afternoon. I took the children downstairs with me so that Her Majesty could see them; and I've never been so embarrassed in my life. At first there was absolutely no way of getting a single word out of either of them; then this bandit plants himself in front of the Queen, and stares at her with the utmost impertinence, holds out his little hand and says: 'Give me a penny.' Her Majesty laughed and laughed."

"Well, my precocious young gentleman, here is a penny," Pez said, giving him one.

"Oh, but you mustn't give him anything; and he only wants it to buy trash. This silly girl doesn't beg, but she doesn't refuse what she is given. And don't think she wastes it either! She puts it all in her money box, and she's got quite a sum saved up already. She takes after . . ."

"Takes after Papa."

"Run along, children, run into the house; you'll catch cold here. How you're perspiring, daughter, run along quickly. I am coming in myself in a minute."

A few bounds carried the children to the doorway on the Caceres staircase, and a few more leaps took them up to the apartment. Pez sighed as they disappeared. Rosalía was carrying a rose in her hand which had lost half its petals; but it was still very fragrant, and from time to time she buried her nose in its heart as if she wanted to take in all its sweetness at one breath. And such a flower was a worthy setting for such a nose.

"In the end," Pez said, returning to his usual melancholy theme "you'll be obliged to turn me out, I shall become such a nuisance."

She must have answered that she saw no reason for turning anyone out, for he took courage from her reply and begged pardon for his extreme attachment to the Bringas family. To deprive him of the consolation of their affection would be a cruelty, he said. And to speak frankly, the focus of attraction—yes, that was the word for it—'the focus of attraction is not so much my good friend Bringas as my incomparable friend, his wife. You understand me better than he does, better than anyone does. It's strange, but on the days when I can't manage to exchange at least a few words with you it seems to me that something is lacking, as if the roots of life couldn't find any moisture to drink and the sap of being was drying up.' Pez's conversation had taken a turn towards the poetical and philosophical, and Rosalía listened to him with swelling vanity and dilating nostrils, as she crushed the rose against her face and its fragrance enveloped them both. And still Pez went on speaking:

"This irresistible sympathy is stronger than I am. If you forbid me to come, you'll see how quickly this life will be extinguished, this life which was once dedicated to love of family, and is still always at the service of my country. You will be doing me the greatest injury that can be done to a man, and it will benefit nobody."

She cannot have shown herself very severe with him, for he was soon expressing the wish that they could see each other more frequently. When Bringas was well again, why shouldn't they meet more often, and under conditions where they could talk more freely?

He still had much to say to her; but it was impossible to prolong their stroll any more and they went inside. As they reached the door of the apartment, Isabelita ran out looking for her mother, shouting in delight: .

"Papa can see! Papa can see!"

Rosalía and Pez hurried in, overjoyed to hear such tidings and found Don Francisco walking up and down in *Gasperini*, with the bandage pushed up on his forehead, so nervous and excited that he seemed almost demented.

"I can see perfectly. There's a slight pain and a reddish border round things, but I can see everything. My dear Pez, you look younger than ever, and my wife looks like a girl. I am mad with happiness. The light does bother me a little, I admit, but that's only a matter of days, I'm sure. Embrace me, my dear. Everyone embrace me."

"Don't shout victory too soon," Rosalía warned, stabbed by a sudden thought in the midst of her joy. "You mustn't bring on a relapse. If I were you, I wouldn't take the bandage off yet."

"What in the world is going on here?" demanded the doctor, coming in just then, unannounced. "An orgy, nothing less! Put on that bandage again, you can't be certain of a cure yet. You must wait. Have a little patience, man. And then the waters . . ."

"What waters? I shan't go to any baths now," Bringas exclaimed, though he let the doctor's authoritative hands put the bandage back in place. "I don't need to take any waters—don't come to me with these fantasies."

"We'll see about that later," said the doctor kindly. "But now, back to prison. You shan't escape before the appointed time or you might get a longer sentence. Everything is going on well, very well indeed; and if you're not in too much of a hurry you'll arrive where you want to be all in good time."

The late evening light by which our friend had proved to himself with such immense pleasure that his sight had returned, slowly faded from the room until finally the apartment was only lit by the glow which the sunset had left in the sky behind the Casa de Campo; but that was as brilliant as the light from a burning house. Rosalía wanted to bring in a lamp, but Bringas said quickly that they didn't need a light, adding:

"Excuse me, Señor Don Manuel, but it seems to me that we are better off like this in the twilight; a lamp would only make it hotter. Paquito, open the window as wide as you can and let the air in, all the air."

Soon after this Bringas grew tired of listening to his son's University anecdotes, and called out:

"Señor de Pez, are you there?"

"He went out," Paquito said.

"Rosalía!"

"Mama!" the youth shouted.

Rosalía came in, and her majestic figure appearing like a phantom in the darkness brought an air of theatrical mystery to the solitary habitation in which the father and son were sitting almost invisible in the shadows.

"Has Don Manuel gone?" Bringas asked.

"No, he is in the *Saleta*, out on the balcony looking at the sky. I do wish you could see it. The sun has left such a glow in the West that it's as if half the world were burning."

"Go back and entertain him. Today I gave him a hint about the boy's going up in the service, and it seemed to me he didn't take it badly. He gave me a *we'll see* that had a ring of *yes* about it. Only don't forget that we must have supper at nine."

Pez said goodbye before that; and when he had gone Rosalía took off her handsome dress and low cut shoes and put on her old house dress and felt-soled slippers and began to prepare the supper. She complained of a bad headache and only took a little vegetable soup. Oh that *tertulia* of Doña Tula's, with Pez and Serafinita, neither of whom ever stopped talking, had made her head feel like a bomb! And Don Manuel by himself could give anyone a headache with that endless litany of his woes. He had so many troubles now that he had left Job far behind.

"But you should go to bed, my dear, and rest after all that noise. Only it's essential to listen to Pez patiently—you know, what I told you about. We are his Veronica's Napkin; he comes to us to disburden himself of his griefs."

In the end Rosalía did as her husband ordered, and went to bed, first charging Paquito with the task of giving his father the medicines which he took later on in the evening. Her head sought rest at last on her pillows; but sleep was long in coming and only arrived after a considerable period of troubled vacillation.

XXVI

Her thoughts went round and round. The silver candlesticks . . . the danger that her husband would discover
that they had made a trip to the pawnship . . . the means
of avoiding this discovery . . . Señor de Pez —what a
fascinating man! What an exalted outlook he had. When
you had said that he was capable of organizing an administrative system with eighty-four ministries, you
had shown what that superb head could do. And what
fineness and breeding, and what knightly generosity! It
was certain that if she found herself in some financial
difficulty Pez would come to her aid with that gallantry
and delicacy of which Bringas had not the faintest conception, and which he had never shown at any time, not
even when he was courting her or during their honeymoon.
That honeymoon, which was passed in Navalcarnero!

What a dull course her life had always taken! Even the
village that had been chosen as the place in which to
inaugurate their married life had been so rough and antipathetic to her, and so contrary to all ideas of good tone.
How well she remembered that village inn that hadn't
a single comfortable chair, with its smell of cattle and
straw, and the wine they served that smelled of fish and
the cutlets that tasted of leather. And then that pedestrian
Bringas had only talked to her about the most commonplace things. In Madrid, even on the day before their
wedding, he was not the man to think of spending a few
pennies on a bunch of roses. During their stay in Navalcarnero he had given her an earthenware jug and taken
her for walks in the cornfields, where they gathered
poppies which lost their petals immediately. She cared

159

very little for the country at any time; the only thing
that might have reconciled her to it would have been
shooting. But Bringas was afraid of a gun; and on the
only occasion when he did go out shooting, with the
Mayor of the village, he very nearly killed the Mayor.
He couldn't hit the wind.

As soon as they returned to Madrid, their regimented
matrimonial life had began—that life which was composed of scanty means and considerable pretensions, a
domestic comedy performed night and day in the course
of the methodical passing of the pennies and the hours.
Subjected to such a commonplace man, she had learned
her tepid role and had come to play it without even
thinking of what she was doing. That commonplace
husband had made her the mother of four children, one
of whom had died in infancy. She loved her children
passionately, and consequently she had come to have an
increasing attachment to her husband: she wanted him
to live and to be well. As his faithful wife she would
continue at his side playing her rôle there, with the skill
she had acquired during so many years of hypocrisy.

But for herself she ardently desired something more than
merely to live and have health. She longed for a little, even a
very little, of what she had never had: liberty. She wanted to
escape, if only in her own imagination, from her shamefully
narrow way of life. Because—she could say it in all sin-
cerity—she sometimes envied the beggars she saw in the
streets, since, if they had a penny, they could spend it as
they pleased, while she . . . But at this point sleep over-
came her, and she did not even feel the weight of her
husband's body when it was laid down upon the mattress
beside her.

When she opened her eyes in the morning her first
thought was for the imprisoned candlesticks; and she
asked her husband anxiously how he felt.

"It seems to me that I don't see as well as I hoped I would," he answered, giving a great sigh. "I've been awake since four o'clock, listening to all the hours striking. My eyes hurt and smart, and I don't feel I could bear the light on them."

They passed the morning in great uneasiness waiting for the doctor, and when he came he showed that he was disappointed and perplexed, and kept hesitating over medical explanations of this retrogression in the state of the patient. Had he been eating too much? Was it the effect of too much belladonna perhaps? Was it—? At any rate Don Francisco must go back to the old regime of darkness, rest and quiet and no visitors. The sadness with which our friend received the doctor's orders was indescribable. He listened in silence while his wife said angrily, with dilated nostrils:

"You see what happens when you want to get well in two days! I keep telling you—but you are a child!"

The unfortunate man was too cast down even to reply. All that day he sat silent in his arm chair with folded hands. His wife and son tried in vain to comfort him with affectionate reassurances; his melancholy only seemed to grow deeper when they talked to him. That afternoon Pez, wise after the event, said to Rosalía when they were discussing this new unfortunate turn of affairs:

"I don't know why you didn't call in an oculist from the very first. This good señor (by which he meant the doctor) seems to me to know as much about eyes as a mole."

"But I begged Bringas to do it," the lady answered, trying to express with eloquent face and shrugged shoulders how mean her husband was. "But try to get Bringas to do anything! He flatly refused, and said that oculists only visit you to get money out of you. And it isn't really that he's so hard up; but he can't decide to spend anything until there's some final crisis, and the disease says to him: "Your money or your sight!"

Don Manuel laughed at this picturesque description of his friend's economic ways; but when he was talking to Bringas later on that evening he hinted at the advisability of consulting a specialist. And this time the invalid did not reject the suggestion. Disheartened and impatient he had began to feel that a ray of light was worth all his savings, and he only said:

"Do whatever you all think is best."

That night Milagros arrived to keep her co-religionist company. Rosalía had not seen her since the previous week and had supposed that the agonizing problem of the end of June had been solved. But when she saw the aristocratic lady's face, she noticed with surprise that it did not express the contentment of victory. And the Tellería was not long in telling her that her difficulty had not really been resolved at all, but only put off for the time being. By much pleading she had managed to get a reprieve until the 10th of July. But it was already the 7th so that she had only three days of grace left. By all the saints, by all her friend held dear, she begged her ...

Rosalía put her finger to her lips to council discretion, for Isabelita was in the room, and the child had the bad habit of repeating everything she heard. Only a few days before she had made her father laugh with this innocent declaration:

"Papa, Don Manuel says that I take after you, because I save all the pennies I'm given."

XXVII

That evening, when he heard the little girl come into the room, Don Francisco called her to come and sit on his knees.

"Where is Mama?" he enquired.

"She is in the *Saleta* with the Marquesa," the child replied, speaking clearly and rapidly. "They told me to run away and come to you. The Marquesa was crying because it's the 7th."

"It's the 7th," Milagros had said, crossing her hands in the depths of despair. "If I haven't got the money by the 10th . . . Oh, I shall have a nervous breakdown, I know. You can't think what my head is like."

The two ladies had shut themselves up in the empty room without a light, for the master of the house was an ardent partisan of every kind of darkness. There the unhappy Marquesa displayed her grief like a treasure, expressing it in a dozen different ways with florid, elegiac inspiration. The day was hateful to her, she said, she loved the night, for then she could lose herself in the contemplation of her pain. When she looked up at the stars she felt some inexplicable consolation. They seemed to promise her happiness; or perhaps it was only that their metallic lustre found its way into her soul. It was strange the relationship of the stars to hidden gold. She no longer had any hope in anything, except her friend. She was counting upon her to save her. How? She could not say. But she had appeared to her in her dreams, with that angelic smile and that infinitely distinguished air."

"Holy Mary!" Rosalía exclaimed. "Don't foster such illusions, for God's sake! I can't, I can't, I can't!"

"But you can, you can!" Milagros replied, with an insistence, which exercised a certain fascination on the other's spirit. "You have only to wish to do it, and you can. It's not such a tremendous undertaking after all. I've got five thousand reals and I only need five thousand more. Bringas . . ."

"I don't know what words to use to convince you that it would be easier to drink the sea dry than to get the money out of my husband."

"I forgot to say that I've brought the letter from my administrator with me today, the one that promises me the money by the 15th or the 20th at latest. I don't know what better guarantee you could have. Of course there would be a formal agreement as well. If I can't settle this affair I won't be able to support my shame. When they come to take me to court, they will find me dead. Sometimes I ask myself if there won't be a cataclysm or an earthquake or some other natural disaster before the 10th! I think of this revolution they are always talking about, and I almost wish that something *would* happen. I'd be satisfied with a week of rioting and shooting during which no one could go out in the streets! But no, not even that, my dear. Have you heard that they've sent the generals to prison—Serrano, Dulce and Caballero de Rodas? They say they are going to be shipped off to the Canaries and that the Duque de Montpensier has been removed too. With all those precautions there won't be anyone left to rise."

"Are they really sending the Generals to the Canaries? I only wish it were to the Infernal Regions!" Rosalía exclaimed jubilantly. "How glad I am to hear it! Now they've got rid of them, all these alarms will stop. Let them try to conspire now! And they've disposed of the Infante too? I must go and tell Bringas about it."

And she ran off to *Gasperini* to tell her husband the good news; and he was as pleased to hear it as if he had won the lottery. (Well, perhaps not quite so pleased but very nearly.)

"Good, good, good," he kept saying. "That's the way to govern! That will teach them to conspire against the best of Queens! What a brave man the President of the Council must be! I only wish I could embrace him. So they are off to the Canaries, are they? You might as well say, to the other side of the world. And if the ship that's taking them sinks to the bottom on the way, so much the better. I'd like to go out on the terrace and shout *Long Live the Queen!* at the top of my voice."

And he really seemed inclined to do so. Afterwards Milagros came in to see him and flattered his dynastic passion with her picturesque chatter, demanding not one death for the generals but a hundred, and the scaffold for all conspirators. This excitement cheered the poor man up a great deal. But, alas, the next day proved to be one of the saddest of his life, for after passing a very restless night, he found when daylight came that his sight was almost completely gone. The doctor, when he arrived, was so alarmed by his condition, that he did not make use of any of the comforting formulas which doctors employ when they are unwilling to admit that their treatment has failed. He was a conscientious man and knew the time had come to abdicate his authority for fear of doing more damage, so he said:

"It's essential to consult an oculist. You must see Golfin."

Don Francisco thought that the sky was falling. His case must be desperate indeed. However, avarice was conquered by fear, and he did not think of opposing the opinion of the doctor, backed up as it was by his whole family. They were all in a state of consternation, and could only fix their hopes on the prodigious scientific attainments of this famous oculist, the most famous in Spain. They agreed to consult him without a moment's delay.

Golfin! Bringas knew him well by report, for all sorts of marvels were told of him. He was said to have given back their sight to many people who had been supposed · hopelessly blind. He had made great fortunes in South America and North America as well as in Spain. For operating on the Marques de Castro for cataract he had charged eighteen thousand reals, they said; and for curing the Cucurbitas' little boy of conjunctivitis he had charged so much that the family had been in debt for six years afterwards. But Bringas had begun to feel that if Golfin would only cure him, he did not care if he took everything he had down to his last shirt.

The only thing they were not all agreed on was whether the invalid should go to the oculist's consulting rooms or get him to visit Bringas at home.

Don Francisco was set on going himself because he thought it would be less expensive.

"Paquito and I can easily take a coach there," he said.

"No. You are not well enough to go out. He must come here," Rosalia answered.

"No, no, my dear. These potentates of science never leave their houses except to attend princes or millionaires."

"I say he must come to see you. I am going downstairs to Her Majesty: she will write a letter to him for me."

"Yes. I am sure she will. And if *La Señora* will just add a postscript to say that the case is that of a person in poor circumstances, it will be all the better. Bless you, my dear, for thinking of it."

The letter was written, and Golfin came immediately, and in his rough, kind way comforted the patient a great deal, and gave him back the hope that he was beginning to lose; for he declared that the disease was not really very serious, though the cure would be slow.

"Patience is the main thing," he said. "Plenty of patience, and exact carrying out of all my instructions.

166

There's a touch of conjunctivitis, which ought to be taken in hand at once."

Poor Bringas! Once more it was a question of bed, low diet, absolute rest, and atropine. And it was the beginning of a very sad period in his life. There was no point in taking off the bandage any longer, for he could hardly see at all when he did, and the light hurt his eyes so much that he was only too glad to go back to the darkness. His only consolation was the memory of Golfin's heavenly promise, made when he was saying goodbye:

"You will see again, and you will see what you have never seen before."

This was his manner of praising the value of this precious sense of sight, which we treasure more than all our others. To see—but when, God all-powerful? When, Blessed Santa Lucia? The poor man showed no lack of patience; and his wretched condition made him turn his thoughts towards religion, so that he employed many of his solitary hours in prayer. His wife never left him except to perform the absolutely indispensable household tasks or to entertain some important visitor; as, for instance, Milagros when she appeared and called her friend out and made much of her with flattery and caresses. There could no longer be any question of going away to some watering place, unless Bringas should get much better by the early part of August, and that seemed most unlikely.

One of the most constant friends of the afflicted family in this hour of trouble was Pez; and one evening when he had been able to get Rosalía aside and talk to her alone, she said to him:

"We are entering a period of great distress now; I don't know how we shall ever get through it."

Don Manuel's reply to this statement was a Quixotic outburst, in which he offered to come to her aid in all

difficulties of whatever kind. This noble assurance was
like a ray of celestial light to the lady's spirit. Now she
could count on some certain support in the difficulties
which her clandestine way of life got her into. Now she
had something to fall back upon on some critical occasion.
She saw a strong arm stretched out to aid her, a shield.
Life seemed easier, as if it opened out to her . . .

"And I will take care," she said to herself, "that this
friendship is not incompatible with my honour."

XXVIII

The sight of her husband in this weak and helpless state awoke the old affection of other days in Rosalía. The real attachment she had always had for him cleared itself of ill feelings and became strong and warm again and the haughty lady felt a deep tenderness for the good companion of her life during so many years. If he had not given her self-esteem any very lively satisfactions, he had at least never wounded it in any way. Her mind dwelt on their prosaic, tranquil life together, full of scarcities, it is true, but also full of simple pleasures, which, though in detail they might seem of little value, taken together made up a pleasant whole. With Bringas she had had neither comforts, nor high position, nor pleasures, nor grandeurs, nor luxury; none of those things, in fact, which she felt that by right she should have had, because of her beauty and her aristocratic nature. But, in exchange, how peacefully and smoothly the days had gone by, with no alarms, no debts, no creditors. Not to owe a penny to any man, was the principle of that very ordinary husband she had married; and following this rule they had been unfashionable, it is true, but also honourable, and happy in their poverty. Certainly if fate had given her a husband like Pez, she would have had a more brilliant position in the world.

"But God knows," she thought wisely, "what agonies are suffered in those houses where they always spend more than they have. You need to see those things close to, and go through them yourself to know what they are."

As her husband's illness got worse Rosalía drew closer to him both morally and mentally, perceptibly tighten-

169

ing the matrimonial bonds. Sympathy with misfortune worked this miracle, and also the long continued habit of sharing all the happenings of life with him, the bad as well as the good. And how well she looked after her husband! What a delicate touch she had, and how she poured out her tenderness to comfort the sick man's spirit! These intimate joys softened his sufferings, and, inspired as he was at that time by religious ardour, he imagined that his wife's devotion to him was an expression of divine assistance. He was only cast down when she left him to perform her usual domestic tasks, and kept calling her back to him on the least excuse and begging her to do as little as possible in the house and consecrate all her time to him.

During this period Rosalía did not give a thought to dress; she had neither the time nor the inclination to spend on trifles. Had she really turned against her luxurious instincts, or was it the spirit of abnegation? Something of both perhaps. But if it was abnegation it was carried to an extreme point, for she actually appeared before Señor de Pez in the old clothes which she wore round the house, in the most prosaic manner imaginable. The only attention to appearance which she still allowed herself was that of always wearing her best corset for fear of her figure spreading. But she did her hair in the simplest style, and her dress showed traces of all those incidents that occur in the management of a humble home. One afternoon she said to Don Manuel: "Don't look at me. I'm a scarecrow." He answered: "However you are dressed, you are always beautiful." And she was truly grateful for his gallantry.

Weakness of body brings with it other lamentable weaknesses even in the strongest characters; a prolonged illness produces the effects of old age in men and also makes them childish; and Bringas was not exempt from this physical-moral deterioration. His weak state awoke ardours of tenderness in him, and this tenderness translated itself into certain foolish enthusiasms.

"Darling, don't tell me that you are a woman; you are an angel. Up to now I have ruled in the house, and you have been a slave; but from now on the only will here shall be yours. I will be the slave."

On the first day of what we might call the reign of Golfín, Don Francisco had his money box brought to him as usual so that he could get out the money for the daily expenses. But soon this tender doting, this puerile weakness of which we have just spoken, inspired him with a confidence which he had never felt before.

"You needn't bring the box to me, my dear," he said. "Take the key and get out what you think we will need."

What he did not neglect to do, however, even at that time was to ask for the keys back and put them safely underneath his mattress again; because all weakness, whether senile or infantile, has its limits.

Rosalía was thus made free of the secret treasure, and turned the money over and counted what she found in the double bottom, amazed at the amount there. Her husband had saved far more than she had ever suspected; he was really a capitalist. There were five bills for four thousand reals, that is, a thousand duros; and besides that there were a number of small bills which all together made up the sum of three thousand seven hundred reals. Those five big bills were the most splendid quintet the lady had ever seen; but as she looked at them her resentments and complaints against her husband, which had so often embittered her spirit, awoke to fresh life. To have so much money and still to want to dress his wife like a priest's housekeeper! What a ridiculous man! If he really meant what he said about her being the real mistress of the house in days to come, she would have

171

to change her ways and use the family savings in a way
more becoming to the dignity of the family. Really, to
save money up like that without getting anything from
it at all! It was too absurd. At least he might have lent it
out at interest, or invested it in one of the Societies which
pay dividends.

The discovery of this treasure changed the whole
current of Rosalía's thoughts, and drew them out of
the circle of modesty and abnegation in which the illness
of her husband had enclosed her. One day he said to her
in a sudden burst of enthusiasm:

"When I am cured, I am going to buy you a silk dress,
and this winter, if everything goes well, you shall have a
velvet one too. It is essential for you to be well-dressed
sometimes, and not only with the presents the Queen and
your friends give you. I want you to wear dresses bought
with the money I have saved by honourable work."

After that speech his wife began to consider that if the
treasure was not exactly hers, at any rate the greater
part of it ought to be at her disposal.

"I have deprived myself too long and suffered too much
from not having things I needed, to endure all these difficulties I go through for lack of money, when *he* has so
much. If he doesn't give me what I need, I will make
him see that he owes me more consideration."

She was in this frame of mind when Milagros came in
one morning, at such a fortunate moment that it seemed
that Providence had prepared everything for the Marquesa's satisfaction. Before she had even finished announc-
ing, between sighs and groans, the imminence of her
catastrophe, Rosalía said to her in a decided tone:

"Will you sign an agreement promising to repay me
in a month? Because the more intimate friends are, the
more careful they ought to be about proper forms in
business matters. Will you pay me two and a half per

cent a month and add on to the agreement the seven
hundred reals you owe me already? Because friendship
is one thing, my dear, and business—you won't be
offended with me for saying so—"

Needless to say the Tellería agreed to everything, with
the most sincere and grateful expressions. Not to have
believed her would have been like doubting the light
of day.

"Well, if that's agreed on, I can let you have the five
thousand reals," Rosalía announced, with distinct traces
of the money-lender in her manner.

Those who, either in reality or in ecstatic imaginings,
have seen the skies open and cohorts of angels singing the
praises of the Lord, can hardly have looked more radiant
than Milagros did when she heard this wonderful pronouncement. But . . .

XXIX

There is no felicity without its *but*. And the Marquesa's
but was that to complete the sum she needed she had to
have *six* thousand reals. Because there was a small bill
attached ... well, she needn't go into all that ... As for
the interest, she didn't care whether it was two and a half
per cent or six per cent. "It's immaterial to me, dear. The
more you can get out of it the better I'll be pleased."
Rosalía hesitated a little, but in the end everything was
agreed on to the satisfaction of both, and that same
evening the paper was made out and signed in *la Furiela*,
with all the precautions necessary to keep Isabelita,
always curious about everything, from finding out what
they were doing.

"Oh, what a wife you have! God has sent you one
of his favourite angels. Don't complain about your illness,
my dear friend, it's nothing serious and you'll soon be
well. Thank God instead. Anyone who has Rosalía at
his side can support all calamities with courage."

Don Francisco was much moved by this speech, which
Milagros made while she was saying goodbye to him and
giving passionate kisses to the favourite angel.

The favourite angel had been influenced by various
impulses when she did what she did. The first was simply
a wish to help her friend; but she had also been affected
by the idea (so often expressed by Bringas during his
illness) that she could dispose of everything as she wished
and this had taken possession of her mind and given
birth to other ideas of dominion and authority. She felt
that she must show by some act—even though it went
beyond the limits of prudence—that she had left off being

a slave at last, and asserted her rights in the distribution of the conjugal fortune. This was not the only idea she used to quiet her conscience however; she could also consider that she had placed the money out at interest. Her mean-spirited husband would have no just cause for complaint if the five thousand reals brought some more with them when they returned to the box. But perhaps all the reasons suggested would not have been sufficient if she had not felt that she could count on certain sources of aid, in the extreme case of Bringas finding out what she had done and disapproving of it. If she had not counted, in fact, on the offer which the friend of the house had made to her only the day before.

He had led her to the window at twilight to admire the melancholy beauty of the distant landscape; and while they were standing there had spoken these words:

"If, for any reason, either for the expenses of *his* illness, or because you can't balance your household accounts— if for any reason at all, in fact, you find yourself involved in any difficulty, you have only to let me know. Tell me yourself, or send a note, and immediately . . . No, no, there is nothing strange about it. Forgive me if I have spoken crudely, in a way that seems even a little indelicate. It is difficult to treat such matters in any other way. It would be entirely between ourselves, and the last person to know anything about it would be Bringas. In the bosom of confidence, of pure and honourable friendship, surely I can offer what I can spare, and you can accept what you need!"

Phrases followed this offer which belonged more to the romantic than to the financial order. In them the unfortunate man expressed once more the consolation which his suffering spirit received from breathing the atmosphere of that house and discharging the burden of his grief in the indulgent ears of the being who had come

175

to occupy the first place in his heart and thoughts. Rosalía left the window with her head completely turned. She would gladly have stayed there for hours listening to those poetic speeches, which seemed to her to be the payment of long unpaid debts of homage which the world owed her.

Several days passed without any noticeable improvement in Don Francisco's condition. Golfin martyrized him cruelly three times a week by running a probe dipped in nitrate of silver along his eyelids and following that with another dipped in a strong solution of ordinary salt. Our friend saw stars when this was done, and had to call on all his strength of mind and dignity as a man not to scream like a child. An application of cold water compresses relieved the pain and for a time he felt a relative sense of well being, thought that he was better and praised Golfin. After ten or twelve days of this treatment the learned oculist assured Bringas that he would be much better by August and by September should be entirely cured, and the invalid had such faith in the famous man that he never doubted the truth of this prognostication. After the 20th of July the cauterization was done with sulphate of copper which was much less painful, and the invalid was allowed to sit up in a darkened room without his bandage, but not to fix his attention on anything.

The excessive admiration which Don Francisco felt for Golfin led his thoughts insensibly to quite another region of ideas, and one much less pleasing.

"When I think of the bill that that Santa Lucia in a frock coat is going to send in," he said to his wife, "I positively tremble. He will cure my eyes and do a fatal injury to my pocket. It's not that I want to be mean when it's a question of sight itself. But the fact is, my dear, that this scientific phenomenon is going to leave me without a shirt to my back."

They had both heard that these celebrated specialists always have the income of the patient in mind when they send in their bills, and make them heavy in the case of rich people, but light when they have to deal with some poor clerk or other person in a humble position. They are humane and know how to adjust themselves to the hard realities of life. Rosalía knew of someone whom Golfin had charged very little for an operation followed by a long and difficult course of treatment. Firm in these ideas of distributive justice as applied to human suffering, Don Francisco was always complaining about his ill luck when Golfin was present, and deplored his misfortunes so much that it was almost as if he were begging for alms.

"Señor Don Teodoro, I will bless you all my life for the good you are doing me, and my children will bless you too. Cure me as quickly as you can, I beg you, so that I can get back to work, for if my illness goes on, I don't know what will become of my family. They have cut my salary at the office of the Privy Purse in half, and we have got horribly behind. If I don't recover the use of my eyes soon, I don't know what will become of us . . . I can finish my days in an almshouse—but my poor children . . ."

XXX

But these complaints Bringas made did not fit in at all with the idea Golfín had of the position of the Señores de Bringas. He had often seen them in theatres and other public places, both always very well dressed, and he had also seen Rosalía riding in a carriage in the Castellana with the Marquesa de Tellería or the Condesa de Santa Barbara or other aristocratic ladies; he even thought he remembered encountering them at various fashionable reunions, competing in dress and behaviour with people of the highest rank. He had supposed, judging by these observations, that Don Francisco was a man of property, or at any rate one of those functionaries who know how to extract from politics the sap which others try in vain to press from the hard, dry material of daily work. But then Golfín was rather an innocent man in things of the world; he had passed the greater part of his life abroad and did not know our customs; and he was consequently not acquainted with this speciality of Madrid life, which in other cities are known as *Mysteries*, but among us are mysteries to no one.

As Bringas grew better, his wife noticed a steady decrease in those raptures of conjugal affection which had come over him during the worst period of his illness. She observed that those exaggerations of feeling did not seem to accompany the hope of improvement, and that as this hope grew stronger, the senile, tearful child recovered his true masculine nature. It seemed that all that talk of *You shall be the mistress and I will be your slave* had been only the drivellings of the disease. As soon as the man could look after himself again and was no longer in pain—

178

even though he could not see and had to sit always in his arm chair—he developed a perfect itch to inspect everything and interfere in all the small household happenings. Rosalía got so tired of listening to him that she left him alone with Paquito or Isabelita most of the time, pretending that she was very busy about the house, but in reality spending long periods shut up in the *Camón*, where Emilia had begun to function again in a sea of cloth and ribbons whose curling waves rolled away to the door.

But the economist seemed to be impatient to use his regained authority and would often send for his wife to come to his presence, and there, with the air of an inflexible judge, would make a public show (for Torres or some other friend would often be present) of his sovereignty in domestic affairs.

"I smell burnt sugar. What are you making? Isabelita told me that she saw a big packet of sugar arriving from the shop this morning. Why haven't you told me about it?"

Rosalía replied wearily that the Señor de Pez was, as he knew, dining with them that day, and such a guest couldn't be treated like Cándidita to whom they gave half a doughnut and two dried figs by way of a sweet.

"But my dear, it smells as if you'd thrown half a hundredweight of vanilla in the fire; the whole apartment reeks of it, you must have made enough caramel custard for an army. You never think things out beforehand. If you had gone down and asked the Chef how to make something or other, he'd have been sure to send you up some. And what is that noise of scissors I hear continually? And what brings Emilia here every day? Is she still working on the Marquesa's dresses? Really, it's too much if we're to have a modiste's workroom here for her ladyship's benefit. And while we're on the subject of clothes, tell me what you have been getting for the children which makes people take notice of them in the Plaza del Oriente?"

"Makes people take notice of them?"

"Yes, take notice of them because they are so well dressed. Golfin said to me this morning: 'I saw your children in the Prado yesterday, looking *very elegant*.' *Very elegant!* Believe me, my dear, I didn't like the sound of that at all: it alarmed me. What will this good señor think of us when he sees our children going round looking like lambs dressed up to be raffled, as if they belonged to the wealthiest families in Madrid? He will get some absurd notion about us. I had my suspicions that something like this was going on, because yesterday when I had the bandage off I noticed that Isabelita was wearing some fine scarlet stockings—Where did those come from? And why not at least make her take them off when she comes in? We must go into everything when I can see properly again. Pray God that will be soon."

With this perpetual fussing going on, it is easy to imagine what a state Rosalía was in. She generally managed to appease her husband for the time being with subtle explanations of everything that came up; but all her ingenuity wasn't sufficient to satisfy him completely on some occasions, for not only was the good economist extraordinarily suspicious by nature, but he had a very great knowledge of all the domestic arts. When the lady found herself alone again after one of these scenes, she would relieve her feelings by silently breathing to herself some rancorous phrase like 'You wretched miser, how can I prove to you that you don't deserve a woman like me? Won't you ever take it in that a wife like me is bound to cost you more than an old housekeeper? Well, I will make you understand it some day!'

She was always making plans for gradually emancipating herself, and studying phrases with which to break this silly and ridiculous servitude. But all her courage deserted her when she thought of the storm which would fall on her head if her husband discovered what had been going on in the false bottom of the chest. Christ our Father, what a state he would be in! She had really committed a great fault, she knew, in taking out part of the conjugal fortune; for even though she thought of it as partly hers, still she ought not to have taken anything from it without her husband's consent. But her greatest mistake had been in imagining that you could play such tricks with a man like that. The excuses which had seemed so reasonable to her at the time, now seemed to her too trifling and irrelevant ever to have passed through the mind of a serious person. The motives which she had then obeyed without reflection were without any real foundation, and her conscience argued powerfully against her. No, no, she could not wait and let her husband find her out; it was absolutely essential to put the money back before he did. The amount she needed was seven thousand reals altogether, for besides the six thousand she had given Milagros, she had used a thousand herself to redeem the candlesticks and earrings and for various other small expenses.

This absolute necessity of putting the money back soon preyed on the poor woman's mind to such an extent that she could think of nothing else, though she still counted on the Marquesa's word and on the legal power of the bond she had signed. And Milagros set her mind at rest on the 22nd by saying "It is all arranged, you needn't worry about it." Nevertheless, Rosalía was on tenterhooks, continually dreading a catastrophe and

thinking up all sorts of ways of avoiding it. Up to that
mite her husband had kept up the excellent custom of
giving his wife the keys to the chest when money was
needed. But one afternoon he unexpectedly returned to
his old habits, and got out the box and opened it himself
and began to examine its contents. Heavens, what a
moment! Rosalía's colour came and went. She was almost
mad with fear, and her very terror forced her at any rate
to try to stop him.

"You are always trying to do everything yourself—
you won't listen to what Don Teodoro says . . . What a
hopeless man you are . . . Give me the box."

"Leave me alone," Bringas said, holding on to the box
and energetically defending his treasure.

He counted the gold pieces slowly one by one and
touched the old watch which had belonged to his father
and the antique medals. As nothing was missing among
them, there was no danger so long as he did not lift up
the false bottom.

Rosalía was in such a state of agony that she actually
thought for a moment of shouting 'The house is on fire'.
But she realised that it was impossible to do it because
Paquito was in the room. The flexible hands of the busy-
body were already starting to take up the lid of the double
bottom—Rosalía silently invoked all the Saints and all
the Virgins, the Holy Trinity and even, she thought
afterwards, made some promise to Santa Rita, begging
them to save her. And then, just when Don Francisco's
nail was already in the little hole in the wood by which
the lid was pulled up, he changed his mind—so suddenly
that there really seemed to be something miraculous about
it. He withdrew his finger, and closed the box. Rosalía's
soul returned to her body, and she began to breathe
again. It was obvious that her husband hadn't the least
suspicion of the peculations that had been going on. He

had opened the box because he liked counting the notes from time to time; and then—God knows why—hadn't done so. Perhaps all those invocations to the Saints had been heard, and some angel had inspired the Palace Mouse to leave the counting of his savings unilt another time.

XXXI

Rosalía did not feel safe until she saw her husband
turn the key in the lock: only then did she give thanks
for the great favour she had received. But she realised
only too well that what had not happened that day,
apparently through the special intervention of Providence,
might occur on any other day. The Saints are not always
in the same humour. Finally she thought of a plan which
she believed might satisfy Don Francisco if he examined
the contents of the box again before she was able to
return the money. Her idea was to put some pieces of
paper in the false bottom of the same size as the bills.
If she could find some paper which was of the same
quality to the touch as bank notes, the deception would
be easy, for after all her husband was not going to see
the notes, but only to feel them. She began to examine
all the paper she could find in the house; and in the end
she discovered some on Paquito's desk which seemed to
her to resemble the paper of which banknotes are made
in its flexibility and toughness. She made sure of this as
well as she could by comparing the various kinds of
paper she had found with a note for 200 reals which she
happened to have in her purse. To make the imitation
more perfect it was necessary to give her paper the
patina of use, that greasy smoothness which comes from
having passed through the hands of so many buyers and
sellers—spendthrifts as well as misers.

"What do you want, child?" She asked in annoyance, as Isabelita came in, putting her nose into everything as usual. "Go and keep Papa company, he is
alone."

And she went in to *Camón* and locked the door. There she spent some time crushing her paper up into a ball and then smoothing it out again, until the repeated foldings and unfoldings gave it the required flexibility. It had also acquired the dirty greasy skin which real banknotes have; for before she began her experiments she had been making some croquettes in the kitchen, and she had taken care not to wash her hands so that they would impregnate the paper with that oily dirtiness to which no idealist, so far as I know, has ever taken exception. When she felt that she could do no more to improve the texture of the paper, she was anxious to try out her handiwork. Should she go in to *Gasperini* pretending to be doubtful about the validity of a note and say to her husband: "I don't know what to make of this note, the paper seems different from the others." Her fingers studied the true note and then the false. "Suppose I couldn't see, and some one gave me this piece of paper and a real note, could I tell which was which? Oh, there isn't the slightest doubt, I'd know immediately." And she sighed, and felt so discouraged that she almost gave up her plan. But then she thought: "It's one thing knowing about it beforehand, you feel the difference at once; but if you weren't in the secret it would be different. I'll put them in the box and trust to heaven."

So that evening when Bringas got out the little chest, his wife had the pieces of paper ready to put into it if the Inquisitor opened the false bottom; but he did not touch it. So she took the box from him, as if to save him the trouble of going to the table, and in the brief moment when she was carrying it managed to put her pieces of paper in. She realised however that this was a desperate expedient, and that it was essential to harry Milagros into repaying the loan without loss of time.

On the following day, which was Saint James' Day,
the 25th of July, the heat increased to a really horrible
degree. Bringas sat about in his shirt sleeves, and Rosalía
wore her lightest percale house dress, and never ceased
fanning herself and complaining about the climate of
Madrid and the Western exposure which Bringas had
chosen when he was selecting living quarters in the
autumn. The wretched man had the barefaced impudence
to declare that he liked the heat, that it was healthy, and
that he pitied those silly people who went away in summer.
That very day he had made a deadly announcement to
his family, that they were *not* going to the baths. And
Rosalía was more inflamed by her anger at this decision
than by the intense heat of the weather. To be a prisoner
in Madrid in the dog days, when all her friends had
emigrated! The high Palace-city was already almost
deserted. The Queen had gone to Lequito, and Doña
Tula and Doña Antonia and the rest of the more important court servants had gone with her. Milagros and the
Señor de Pez were preparing to be off too. The unfortunate Señora de Bringas would be left with no one
to visit her except Torres and Cándida and the small
court employees and humble people who lived on the
Third Floor.

She was so annoyed with her husband that she could
not bring herself to say a single pleasant word that day,
but only things that were bitter or cutting. Paquito was
lying on the sofa reading novels and magazines, while
Alfonsin played about as usual, quite indifferent to the
heat, but with his trousers open back and front showing
his rosy flesh and exposing to the fresh air everything
that wanted to get out into it. But Isabelita suffered very
much with the heat. She was tired and hollow eyed, and
lay about all day on chairs or on the floor in a heavy
feverish state, complaining of it. She neglected her dolls

186

and took no interest in anything except what went on around her in the house, which that day was sufficiently curious.

Don Francisco had decided that they would have a *gazpacho* for dinner, since it was the coolest thing they could think of. He could make it better than anyone else, and in former times had always presided over its preparation himself with his sleeves rolled back and turned out a dish which made people suck their fingers. But on this occasion he was not able to go to the kitchen himself, so he gave his orders from his armchair. Isabelita was the messenger chosen to convey them, and, though unwilling and indolent, was kept coming and going continually with culinary instructions.

"He says you are to cut up two onions in the salad, and that you're not to put in more than one tomato and you're to take out the pips carefully ... He says that you are to cut the bread up into very small pieces ... and you're not to use too much garlic ... He says not to put in too much water and to use more vinegar than oil ... that you are to cut up two green peppers if they are small and one if they are large, and to put in some ground pepper as well, about half a thimbleful ...."

The little girl was hungry that night, and though her father said that the *gazpacho* had not turned out at all well, she found it delicious and ate a good deal. When she went to bed her heavy child's sleep at first kept her from feeling the difficulty of digesting the mixture she had eaten; but her nerves protested and her brain began to work with extraordinary vividness, reproducing in its own way all the scenes that had acted upon it during the course of the day.

In her nightmare the child saw Milagros come in and talk to her mother privately, and then the two go away and shut themselves up in the *Camón* and spend some time there counting money and talking. Afterwards the Señor de Pez appeared, a very antipathetic señor, with saffron side whiskers. He and her Papa began to talk about politics and to say that wicked people were going to cut everybody's heads off, and that rivers of blood would flow through the streets of Madrid—and a river of blood did flow in red waves over her Mama and the Señor de Pez when they were talking together in the *Saleta*, her mother telling Don Manuel that they were not going to the baths after all, and he saying: 'I can't stay in Madrid any longer because my daughters are getting so impatient.' Then the Señor de Pez turned blue and flames began to come out of his eyes and when he kissed Isabelita the kiss burned her; and he caught Alfonsin up and set him on his knees and said: 'But, *man*, aren't you ashamed to show what you are showing—.' To which Alfonsin only replied by begging for pennies. Later on when the visitors had left, her father got angry at something her mother said and shouted:

"You are a spendthrift!"

Then her mother got angry too, and went and shut herself up in the *Camón*. And after that another visitor came in, it was the Señor de Vargas, the Cashier of the department where her father worked; and she heard him say to her Papa 'My dear Don Francisco, the Chief has decided that from next month on they can only pay you half your salary while you are absent.' When he heard this her Papa had turned as white as paper, whiter than milk, whiter—and he gave such a sigh! And the two men went on talking, they were saying that rivers of blood would run in Madrid, and that the *so-called* revolution was coming and that there was no help for it. Her mother came into the room when Señor de Vargas was saying goodbye—and this Vargas was a tiny man no bigger than a flea, and when he walked it was as if he were hopping.

After he left her Mama and Papa got angry with each other again and began to quarrel. He kept striking the arms of his chair and she kept walking up and down; the child had never seen her parents quarrelling like that before.

"You are a spendthrift!"

"And you are a miser!"

"It's not possible to live with you and have any kind of order or economy!"

"It's not possible to live with you at all."

"What would happen to you without me?"

"You don't deserve me!"

Then her mother had gone off to the *Camón* and shut herself up there and she could hear her weeping. She followed her to comfort her, and tried to get up in her lap; but she couldn't because her mother had become as big as the Royal Palace—bigger. But her mother had kissed her a great many times, and after that she wasn't angry any more, and had begun to open drawers and chests and take out dresses and yards and yards of silks and ribbons. Then suddenly her Papa came into the *Camón* with his bandage off, and her Mama gave a scream of terror.

"Now, now, I see what you are doing here, Señora, now I see what you are up to! You've brought a whole draper's shop here."

And her Mama, quite overcome, turned crimson and could only stammer:

"I ... I ... you see ..."

But just at that moment the poor child reached the crisis of her attack. She felt as if she were packed to bursting with extraneous objects. Everything seemed to be inside her, as if she had swallowed half the world—her Papa, her Mama, the *Camón*, the Palace, Señor de Pez, the Marquesa, Torres—Her body twisted and writhed in agonized convulsions, trying to rid itself of this oppression. Suddenly it threw it all out like torrent.

XXXII

Immediately the child felt immensely relieved and freed from the fearful mental activity. She was awake, and her mother was there beside her, wiping the sweat from her forehead and speaking to her tenderly. Rosalía had heard the poor child's moaning, the symptom which usually accompanied the nightmare, and had sprung from her bed to run to her assistance. It was midnight. Rosalía made a cup of tea and changed the sheets with Prudencia's assistance, and half an hour later the little girl was sleeping peacefully, and her mother had gone to lie on the sitting room sofa, for the double bed was like an oven. But before she lay down she made a point of telling her husband about the attack.

"The usual thing?" he enquired, from his bed where he was lying covered only with a single sheet.

"Yes, as you say, 'the usual thing', nightmare and convulsions, one of the worst attacks she has ever had. I don't know how you can watch our child developing this tendency to epilepsy and not try to do something about it—when you know that sea bathing cures it!"

"The baths of *Los Jeronominos* are just as good—in fact they are better" Bringas replied stubbornly.

Rosalía's voice dissenting from this opinion was lost in the space around it; while Bringas, after coughing a few times, took with him to the clouds of sleep his belief in the superiority of the baths in the river Manzanares to all the baths in the world.

Bringas grew better so rapidly that after the middle of July, Golfin no longer came to the house to see him.

Don Francisco, accompanied by Paquito, went to the doctor's consulting rooms twice a week instead, wearing a green eye-shade on the way as well as dark glasses to protect his eyes. The doctor's house was in the Calle del Arenal so it was not a long journey, and Golfin, who was particularly attentive because of the Queen's recommendation, always saw him promptly. The specialist was much pleased with the rapidity of the cure and praised the patient's strong constitution which had enabled him to throw off the disease so quickly. At the end of July he told Bringas that he would be going to Germany in the beginning of August. "But I really don't need to see you any more. I consider you as cured. If anything should go wrong, one of my assistants will be here three or four times a week, and you could consult him." Bringas heard this announcement with joy. This dismissal by such a conscientious doctor made it certain that the disease was really vanquished. Spurred by his sense of honour and his delicacy in such matters, he asked the specialist to send him before he went away "You understand me—the account—for your invaluable services." Golfin was equally polite. "There is plenty of time for that surely—why are you in such a hurry about it?—However if you prefer—"

The great economist left the consulting room with his son, anxiously weighing the possibilities of that arithmetical enigma which was now so soon to be solved. What regulating tariff would be applied to his case? Would he be considered as a high placed bureaucrat, or as a rentier of the lesser kind, or as a member of the smaller bourgeoisie, or as beggar? Bringas pondered the problem night and day and longed for the bill to arrive and put him out of his anxiety.

From the moment that her husband informed her that the specialist's bill would have to be paid in the beginning of August, Rosalía realised how extremely urgent it had become to get the notes put back immediately. Fortunately Milagros had paid her a little more than half of what she owed, and had promised to bring the rest before she left for Biarritz.

"I am managing to settle everything in one way or another," she had said, when she brought the first instalment of her debt, "and I'll certainly be able to pay you the rest of the money soon. I might even be able to lend you a little, if you need it. No, don't thank me—I don't need it now; and it's safer in your hands than mine."

With these promises and offerings, Rosalía could see the end of her troubles in sight; though she was in rather low spirits because she was not going away. Still she passed some delicious hours discussing clothes with her friend; and the Tellería, with that admirable art of hers, managed to get back a good many of the things that she had given her friend in those raptures of affection which had preceeded the loan.

"Since you aren't going away after all, that straw hat won't be any use to you, I can fix it up for myself. And you won't be able to wear that light wool dress here either, it's impossible in this climate. But there are some quite cool days at Biarritz, so I'll take it along with me. I'll bring you something you'll like better from there. Oh, and I'll give you some yards of that loose cotton material I got, to make dresses for the children, and some pieces of crêpe I have left over."

Rosalia consented to everything. As she could not make a figure at some Northern watering place herself, she would avenge herself on destiny as best she could by dressing her children handsomely. She was already provided with the necessary juvenile fashion plates and was planning unheard of elegancies for Isabelita and Alfonsin, so that they could display the good taste of their opulent Mama in the Plaza del Oriente among the citizens of the children's republic there.

Sobrino has some summer wraps I'm really enthusiastic about," Milagros went on. "I'm going to get one to take with me. I expect you've seen them—those half-handkerchiefs of imitation Chantilly, with *guipure*."

"Yes, I've seen them, I looked at them yesterday," Rosalía said, with a deep sigh.

"Don't be sad, darling—" Milagros said, caressingly. "In Bayonne you can get things like that for half what you pay here and bring them back through the customs without paying anything. I'll get you one that's prettier than any Sobrino has. Would you like some checked *peau de diable* I don't need, to make something for the children? I'll send it to you then, and in exchange I'll take back these *fichus* and this straw hat shape; they're no use to you in Madrid. If you wear a veil and blouse in the Prado, it's all you can stand; hats never seem to stay on your head in Madrid in summer. Still I do recommend those sailor straws that Sempere has for the children and the little berets too. They are charming. But don't get them anything else. I'll send them each a pair of blue stockings, and I believe I have a good deal of piqué you could make up for them."

And in exchange for all the fine things which she was recovering with so much astuteness, Milagros sent a bundle of shapeless remnants, ribbons and odds and ends; which hardly provided more than a cravat or two for Don Francisco and Paquito.

One morning when Bringas had gone to the oculist with Paquito, Pez appeared unexpectedly. He was dressed for the hot weather in an elegant light coloured alpaca suit, and really looked like a young man. Rosalía was always very pleased to see him, and that day more than ever because he was so well turned out and looked so handsome. His figure played a constantly increasing rôle in the señora's dreams; the two of them had indeed grown more intimate there than they had ever been in real life. What however captivated her much more than his physical attractions or even his fine manners and good breeding were the proposals he had made of coming to her aid if she found herself in any difficulty. She was more inclined to yield to the protector than to the lover. It is certain, in fact, that if Pez had not made those positive offers of assistance, the ground he gained in her esteem would have been much smaller. Though he was a man of considerable experience, Pez had counted principally on the strength of his personal attractions rather than on this other method of warfare. But it is given to few of us to understand all the varieties of human weakness, and that material weapon, which he had used only as an auxiliary aid, turned out to be more effective than all Cupid's shafts.

That day Pez became so ardent from the very first moment he arrived, that Rosalía—who was alone in the house, as both the children and Prudencia had gone out—was in a state of confusion. Everything in her character that was modest and high principled, either by nature or as instructed by Bringas, through so many years of stainless married life, rose up and put her on her guard against him. As a result Pez became in that critical hour a pleading boy and even in the end one of those romantics who put on desperation and speak with enjoyment of their desire for death.

His language and his behaviour, well adapted to the burning mood of the dog days, really frightened Rosalía, who—I say it in her honour—was only a beginner in these criminal friendships. And so my hothead found a virtuous resistance which he was far from expecting, since, as I have often heard him say, he had thought that such a ripe fruit would fall almost of its own accord.

XXXIII

An analysis of Rosalía's virtue produces an extremely singular result. The truth was that Pez had not had the skill or the good fortune to surprise her in one of those moments when the desire to satisfy some caprice, or the financial difficulties she was envolved in, roused the powerful appetite for money that possessed her soul. At such moments her passion for beautiful clothes or the desire to cover up appearances or to conceal her deceptions, blinded her to such a point that she would not have hesitated to buy what she wanted with money paid for with her honour.

It is in this way that the enigma of Pez's lack of success is to be explained. When he tried to take the castle, it was well provisioned. Rosalía had money in hand at the time. Milagros had paid more than half of her debt and promised to pay the rest the following Sunday, and even perhaps add something to it. Sure of coming well out of her most urgent difficulties, the plump, handsome fresh-looking señora felt that she could afford to make a display of her virtue—much less vulnerable to love than to material interest. Pez used a phrase once in speaking of her which lingered in my memory; describing that character which was so full of vanity and that temperament which was inaccessible to every passion except the passion for dress, the great observer remarked that she was like the bulls in the *Plaza de Toros*—she followed the cloth instead of the man.

That day however our friend continued to urge his suit in such a romantic and vehement style that the affair might well have had a melancholy ending if the sudden entrance of the children had not come like an inter-

vention of Providence. Don Francisco came in soon afterwards, and they began to talk about politics—that obscure
sort of politics associated with Gonzalez Bravo, which
on Pez's lips, because of a particular turn his spirits had
taken at that moment, had a very pessimistic tone indeed.
Don Francisco's hair stood on end as he listened. Imprison-
ing the generals and the Duque de Montpensier, it seemed,
had been a stupid mistake. The Revolutionaries had said
their last word in *La Iberia* of the preceding days, and
the Government had launched its ultimate challenge. The
Army certainly sympathized with the revolution and some
people said the Navy was disaffected too . . .

"For God's sake, Señor de Pez, don't say such appalling
things!" poor Don Francisco exclaimed in horror.

"I wash my hands of it!" Pez replied. "I see a cataclysm
coming upon us, and frankly, when I learned that the
Liberal Union, which is a party of order, a serious party,
is siding with the Revolutionaries—well, I can't help thinking that things may not be so black as they are painted."

But at this point Bringas began to grow angry; for
this benevolent attitude his friend was taking seemed to
him like the prelude to a defection. And he unleashed his
rage against the Progressives, the National Militia and
Espartero, without forgetting the *so-called* Hymn of
Riego, and the *so-called* Democrats—in fact against
practically everybody. And he went on with this tirade
for so long that Pez got tired of hearing him and managed
to turn the conversation to the subject of the trip he was
about to take.

He was not in a hurry to go, he said, and he didn't
think that he had to get out of Madrid for the sake of
his health; but his daughters kept begging him to take
them to San Sebastian, and he could not put the expedition
off any longer. The poor girls were longing to show off
their finery in *La Concha* and *La Zurriola*, and if he didn't

take them soon he was afraid they would pine away with grief. Their mother was staying at home, prostrating herself in front of the altar of the Departed Souls, or gossiping with other *beatonas* of the same kind. This trip North was freedom and liberty for the girls, and could not help benefitting their rather delicate health. As far as he was concerned the journey was more of a nuisance than a pleasure, because his daughters made him dizzy with their continual trips into Bayonne to buy silks and smuggle them in. Not that Josefita and Rosita had to do the things that some women did, such as putting on two winter coats one over the other, and six pairs of stockings at a time, and two skirts and four shawls. They were after all in the fortunate position of having a father who was a director of the Exchequer, and this meant that they did not have to suffocate themselves trying to smuggle things in. And when it has been said that the head of the Custom's Office at Irun owed his post to Pez, and was himself a Pez on the maternal side too, it is obvious that the girls could bring in half of France if they wanted to without paying duty.

"But this trip is sure to get me into trouble just the same," Don Manuel concluded, "because I can't show my nose in Bayonne or Biarritz without being besieged by ladies of rank, and ladies of the middle classes too, all begging me for letters to the cousin at Irun. Generally I can't refuse them. This sort of thing is such an old custom with us that it would appear Quixotic in me to think of the revenues. It is something so genuinely Spanish, this seeing in the State the legalized thief. There are a number of proverbs which show how deep-grained this immoral philosophy is among us—for instance that one about *He who steals from the State gets a hundred years indulgence from Purgatory*. It is an old theme of mine, that ours is a lost country. And just try to set yourself up as a moralist! Last year I nearly got my eyes scratched by a certain Marquesa of large estates, because I didn't want to help her smuggle in a huge load of dresses. She turned into a perfect lioness and clamoured for revolution and demagogues. And a certain duchess defied me, as well as my cousin at Irun, and smuggled in-this really will surprise you! —no less than fifty-four trunks full of the latest fashions!"

After telling this story Pez left; and the next day he only came in for a few moments to say goodbye, for he was leaving that afternoon. He managed however to talk to Rosalía alone for a short time, and showed himself so wounded by her amorous indifference and with such a bleeding heart, that the virtuous lady could not help pitying him. His dejected state gave her vanity two satisfactions, that of enjoying her triumphant virtue, and that, no less great, of feeling herself the object of such a formidable passion. How great her attractions must be, when such a serious and sensible man as Pez prostrated himself before her like a boy; when a man like that went crazy over her and *would have bought with his life* (this was his phrase) the least favour!

Milagros did not get off until the 29th, and during the last few days she was full of complaints about the preparations she had to make, and what she suffered in getting ready for the journey.

"My dearest friend," she said to Rosalía, when they were alone in the *Camón*. "You must forgive me for not being able to bring you the rest of the money I owe you before I leave, but I suppose you can manage to wait a few more days for it. I've left instructions with our majordomo to give you the sum by the 5th or 6th of August—by what time they will have received various amounts from Zafra. So don't worry about the money at all, you are certain to get it. It's the first thing I've put down on the list of instructions I've left for Enrique.

And so that he'll be sure to remember it, I tell him every time I see him: 'Don't forget to take the money ... Remember, Enrique, my friend's money is the first thing' ..."

The friend did not like the sound of this at all. But as the promise was such a solemn one, and it was such a short time until the 5th of August, she tried not to worry about it. Milagros went on talking, overwhelming her with exaggerated affection, and swearing that she was going to bring her hundreds of presents from France—all the latest things.

"I suppose we'll find Pez around somewhere, so that he can get us out of all that bother with the Customs. Those vulgar employees are insupportable; they are capable of opening all your trunks—I'm taking the mere trifle of fourteen, and I always bring back three or four more as well. You can't imagine how tired I am with all I've had to do these last few days. My wretched husband doesn't help me at all; you have to hand him everything ready made. This year he wouldn't even take the trouble to write and ask for free tickets, so I had to do it. I wrote letters to the President of the Executive Committee, and in the end, after a lot of argument, they let us have them. But I couldn't get two reserved carriages out of them; they've always let us have two before, but this year they've only given us one. It's so unfair! I told Sudre that that's the payment he gets for defending the Railway Company in the Senate against wind and tide. "I am so nervous by the time we get off that I don't know what I'm doing. I always think I've forgotten something important, and that we're going to miss the train, and that they'll make me pay some huge amount for excess baggage. After all, fourteen trunks! And travelling with my family is like managing a den of demons. Leopoldito is taking his dog of course and Maria her angora cat, and Gustavo is taking a bird cage full of birds for some friend. You even have to think of carrying food for all these irrational creatures! And the whole lot of us in one compartment, it will be like Noah's Ark. Fortunately we know the conductor, and after we've had dinner at Avila, he will let Maria and me go into one of the sleeping cars. I'm taking Asuncion with me of course—I can't manage without a maid: I think we've got twenty-four pieces of hand luggage. I can't close an eye if I don't take pillows, and nothing can stop Sudre from bringing a wash basin so that he can wash himself two or three times on the way. I can't travel without my dressing case, because I don't want to get out at stations looking like a scarecrow. Leopoldito is taking his chess board and his cup and ball as well as his little pistol, and a notebook in which to put down all the tunnels we go through, and the times when we arrive at all the stations. Gustavo is carrying half a dozen books so that he can read the whole way, and that wretch of a husband of mine, who never thinks about anything but his own comfort, will be furious if he hasn't got his slippers and his silk cap and his screen. And it's I who have to attend to everything, because we can't have a manservant for each of us now! Those days are gone, alas; and somehow I don't think that they are going to come back."

XXXIV

The Marquesa embraced Don Francisco warmly when
she said goodbye, fervently wishing him a complete and
prompt recovery, and kissed the children. Then she said
a final goodbye to her friend at the door with all sorts
of fond words and caresses.

Rosalía was disconsolate after she had gone, not so
much at the absence of this dear friend as at being left
behind herself; for this never going anywhere was like a
kind of banishment. What a summer was awaiting her—
lonely, bored, burned up with the heat, and having to
put up with the company of the most interfering and
tiresome of husbands! And worst of all she would have
to endure the shame of having remained all summer in
Madrid, when even the porters and lodging-house
keepers went away somewhere for a holiday. To have to
tell everyone: 'No, we didn't go away this summer'
was a confession of poverty and unfashionableness which
could hardly get past the lips of the daughter of the
Pipaóns and Calderons de la Barca, that illustrious line
of Palace servants.

If they could at any rate have gone to la Granja—
where Her Majesty would certainly have let them have
a corner to put themselves in—they could have said that
they had been away somewhere; even if they only took
a few saddle bags with bacon and salt pork and dried cod
in them, as the villagers do when they go to the baths.
But no, that domestic Caliph of hers indignantly rejected
all suggestions of losing sight of the city and court, and
said all sorts of disagreeable things about the fools and
spendthrifts, as he called them, who went away in the

summer on borrowed money, or half starved themselves for three months, so that they could stay for a few days at some inn and give themselves airs complaining of the food.

The matrimonial crisis, which was mentioned a little further back, had been gradually smoothed over. Bringas was not really so intolerant, and even if he had been he would have sacrificed some of his economical dogmas for peace in the family. The explanations which Rosalía provided for this sudden burst of splendour in her wearing apparel did not entirely satisfy him, but with an effort of will he was able to accept at least some of them. The faith of his matrimonial religion commanded him to believe the inexplicable: and he believed it. If Rosalía had stopped at that point, peace, after this passing alter-cation, would have returned to reign in the household. But the lady could no longer restrain herself; the habit of eluding the Bringuistic regulations had become too firmly fixed. The truth was that she got a secret pleasure from these evasions, besides the satisfaction of her vanity. Each one of her clandestine actions gave her an intimate pleasure, both before it was performed and after. And her conscience knew how to provide—goodness knows from where—innumerable sophistries to justify every-thing she did. They generally took some form like this:

"I have suffered too many privations. It isn't as if I didn't deserve a high position! He must get accustomed to seeing me more emancipated ... The truth is that I'm only trying to keep up appearances for the sake of the family ..."

The thing which most occupied her mind in those first days of loneliness and heat, was the absolute necessity of putting the money back in the box immediately. Milagros had only provided part of it: where was she to

get the rest? She thought of Torres, and when she had
an opportunity hinted discreetly at her need. He didn't
have it. He was sorry! But perhaps he could find some
friend ... Well he would let her know the following
day. Rosalía could hardly wait until she got Torres's
answer, she was so afraid that some catastrophe might
occur at any moment. It would be inevitable as soon as
Bringas examined his treasure, and it would be appalling.
But by good fortune—or more probably through the
special intervention of the Saints whom Rosalía had
invoked—it had not yet occurred to the good man to
lift up the cover of the false bottom. But when it did!
For the pieces of paper with which Rosalía had replaced
the bank notes were no longer of the slightest use now
that Bringas could see; he would not depend on the sense
of touch alone when he examined the contents of the
money box again.

Rosalía was in a terrible state of anxiety all day on the
31st and the next day too, until Torres arrived to give
her hope of a remedy. He began by talking of the difficulties involved, and how hard he had had to work to
persuade his friend to make the loan. This friend was a
man called Torquemada, who never lent money without
an absolute guarantee of its punctual return. In this case,
however, to please Torres, he would not insist as was
usual in such transactions on having the husband's
signature, the señora's would be sufficient. But he could
not let her have the money for more than a month,
and the time could not possibly be extended. And if he
gave her four thousand reals, she would have to pay five
hundred reals monthly interest. Oh, and there would be
two hundred reals deducted from the 4,000 for brokerage...

The skies opened for Rosalía when Torres brought
her this news; and at the moment the interest and the
brokerage seemed a trifle considering the greatness of the

205

favour. Three thousand eight hundred reals would be enough for her purpose; there would even be six duros left over for any unexpected expenses. Everything would be arranged the following day, the 2nd of August. And indeed time was pressing and the danger imminent, as can be seen by a remark which Bringas had made that very morning:

"My dear, Golfin will send in his bill tomorrow, and we must pay it the day after, because he is going away on the 4th he tells me. I positively tremble when I think that that man may imagine that I am well off! How much will he charge me? Have you been thinking of it too? I lay awake half the night worrying about it, and when I did go to sleep I had nightmares like Isabelita's ... And today Golfin said something to me that made me shudder! You can imagine how I felt when she said to me in that lively tone of his: 'I saw your wife coming out from the twelve o'clock mass at San Gines yesterday—she's always so elegant!' I tell you that that wonderful elegance of yours is going to be the knife with which that man will cut my throat!"

However, at half past ten the following morning, while Don Francisco and all his children were out walking in the Cuesta de la Vega, the deed was safely accomplished. Torquemada and Torres appeared at the appointed hour, with all the exactness of usury. Torquemada was a gray haired man of medium height with a four days growth of beard. He was dark and had somehow a clerical air about him; and it was his invariable custom to ask after the health of his client's family, whether he knew them or not. When he spoke, he separated the words and put asthmatic pauses that made paragraphs in the wrong places, in such a way that the listener could not help feeling that he was catching this difficulty in breathing from him. He accompanied his tiresome discourse with a slow elevation of the right arm, while his thumb and index finger described a sort of doughnut in the air, which he held up before the eyes of the person he was talking to as if it were an object of veneration.

His visit that day was short. The only part of the contract to which Rosalía made any objection was the shortness of the time specified; she thought that a month was too little. But Torquemada assured her that he could not possibly make it any longer.

"In the beginning of September I have to make a payment to the Provincial Deputation, because that is the time of the judicial sale of . . . meat for the Hospitals. Think it over . . . Señora, because if you aren't sure that you will be able to repay the loan on the date . . . agreed on, the loan can't be made."

In the end the lady agreed to everything, anxious only to put off the trouble of the day. She signed the bond and took the money; and the two men said goodbye, leaving their regards for the master of the house, though Torquemada had never even met him. Rosalía saw them go with quiet relief and was now only concerned with getting the money back in the box as soon as possible. There was one small difficulty: she had not been given a four thousand real note, but only notes for smaller sums, and she would have to get one of the right size, because, even though the sum in the box remained the same, the Inquisitor would recognize the deception at once. On the pretext of paying a visit she went out early that afternoon. She was in a state of extreme anxiety, fearing that her husband would discover the crime at the last moment. But her good angel was watching for her, and nothing happened during the time that she spent in changing the small notes for one large one, except that the money changer in the Calle del Carmen looked at her with a good deal of surprise. And before night the delicate operation of replacing the missing money had been performed with complete success.

Bringas had seldom felt so nervous as he did in the hours before he received Golfin's bill. At ten o'clock on the 3rd he sent Paquito with a verbal message asking the specialist to send him a note of the honorarium due for his medical assistance, and it was eleven thirty when the youth came back with a letter from the doctor. Bringas did not even breathe while his trembling hand tore open the envelope and unfolded the paper inside. Rosalía stood beside him, filled with anxious curiosity too. Eight thousand reals! When he read the figures Bringas was puzzled, not knowing what to feel. He vacillated between happiness and pain; for though the bill seemed excessive to him, his fears which had made him half expect something enormously greater, disappeared at the sight of the true figure. He had sometimes thought that the bill would not be for less then twelve or sixteen thousand reals; and this idea had almost turned his brain. At other moments he had thought it might not come to more than four thousand. The reality had come midway between these imaginary sums; and in the end the economist consoled himself with arguments from the school of Hermogenes, saying to himself that though eight thousand reals was a lot of money in comparison to four, it was nevertheless a relatively small sum in comparison to 16,000. However a form of reasoning which was entirely his own really dominated this tumult of arithmetical ideas; it was the conviction that, since he had been recommended by the Queen, Golfin ought not to have charged him anything at all.

XXXV

"Still, I am satisfied. I haven't come out of it badly since I've got back my sight, and that assassin did cure me. But eight thousand realitos! It's quite possible too," he added, giving a sigh and getting slightly annoyed, "that if it hadn't been for your elegance, my dear, the blow might only have been for four thousand reals."

However he got out the money at once and wrote a letter to go with it in the most courteous terms, thanking the learned doctor for his invaluable assistance. Then he put the letter and the bank notes into a magnificent envelope (one from the Office) and Paquito was sent off on this second errand. If Bringas looked sadly after his dear banknotes as they went away, on the other hand he got a deep and lively satisfaction from paying what he owed. This is a pleasure which is only known to very honest people of very orderly habits; for such people get a purely spiritual enjoyment from fulfiling their material obligations.

The month of August slowly unrolled its tedious length. This is the month in which Madrid is not Madrid, but an empty frying pan. In those days the only theatre open in summer was Price's Circus, with its insufferable ponies and its clowns who played the same tricks every night. The Prado was the only pleasant place to be; and in the shadow of its trees the amorous couples and the *tertulias* passed the time in more or less boring conversations, trying meanwhile to defend themselves against the heat with waving fans and sips of fresh water. For the Madrilenos who are obliged to pass the summer in the city are the true exiles, and their only consolation is to declare that at least they are drinking the best water in the world.

But Rosalía would not even go to the Prado. She felt that it was making an exhibition of her poverty and unfashionableness. She had already had to employ that formula she had invented to explain her disinherited state too many times.

"We had taken a house in San Sebastian, but with this illness of Bringas' ..."

She was so tired of saying it that she tried to avoid occasions on which she would have to repeat it. So at night the Bringas with some of the other Court employees who were still left in the Palace City would take chairs out on the North side of the terrace and form a group there. And this *tertulia* did not lack animation. Cándida never missed an evening, and there were others who were almost as constant in attendance—wives of various Government officials and of Palace functionaries such the Director of the Royal Table and of the chief of the King's Wardrobe. There were also a few members of the masculine sex at these gatherings, drawn from the small number who were still left in Madrid, but they were mostly of the lowest class. Summer, however, has a very democratizing effect, and the Bringas were so anxious for society of any sort that they did not disdain to mingle, in these open air gatherings, with porters and caretakers, assistant silversmiths, and even with two privy cleaners, all people of salaries of six thousand reals or less. These were sometimes joined by some under-cook who got fourteen thousand, or some usher from the *Saleta* who had to manage on nine. The subjects of conversation were generally the heat that day and the doings of the Court, which had now left la Granja and gone to Lequito, or gossip about people who lived in the Palace-city, or details about the Palace itself.

On the Third Floor, in those large open spaces which, like small Squares, cut up the lengths of the Palace streets, there were other *tertulias* composed of men-servants and maids, cleaners and people who came up from the stables. Near the great windows which face the Plaza del Oriente the noise went on all night. There was great animation and much laughter and guitar playing, and vendors sold refreshing drinks, particularly *horchata de cepas*. But Doña Cándida fulminated against these disorderly gatherings because they kept her awake all night, and was always threatening to denounce the transgressors to the Inspector General.

Every morning the whole Bringas family went down to the Manzanares so that Isabelita and Alfonso could bathe. Don Francisco had brought out his nankeen suit again and in this and his panama hat looked as if he had just arrived from Havana. His eyes were rapidly getting well, thanks to the care with which he followed Golfin's instructions, but he still wore very thick dark spectacles when he went out. The morning air and the lively atmosphere of the baths put him in good humour, and he was always saying that if those idiots who go out of town only knew how excellent the bathing establishments in the river were—*Los Jeronimos, Cypresses, Arco Iris, La Esmeralda* and *El Andalus*—they would lose all desire to emigrate.

Paquito bathed along with the younger children, and threw himself intrepidly into the waves of those dirty little seas that are bounded by rush matting; and he swam splendidly too with only one foot on the bottom. They almost had to beat Alfonsin to get him to come out of the water, while Isabelita had to be persuaded to go in. But Rosalía was obliged to force herself to go down to the river at all. Only her intense love for her children could have made her do it. She was disgusted by the dirty river water and by the common people who bathed in it, while she looked with horror at the rush walls, which seemed more suited to outrage decency than to protect it, and the shouting of the hordes of children got on her nerves horribly.

In the afternoons, when it was almost dark, Rosalía would go down into Madrid to visit some friend, or to make a round of the shops. There were very few customers in the height of summer, and the long curtains, hung over the open doorways, maintained a cooler atmosphere than that of the streets outside. And this comparative coolness and the dimness, combined with their having absolutely nothing to do, invited the shop assistants to lie down and sleep on the bolts of cloth. Occasionally when she went to *Sobrino Hermanos* Rosalía would meet some other señora who had been left behind in Madrid too, some other banished being like herself; and then there would be a new edition of the famous formula: "We had taken a house in San Sebastian ..." But the other lady would usually say with commendable frankness: "We are waiting for the cheap fares in September."

As the shopkeepers were absolutely sitting with folded hands at that season, they were only too glad to entertain themselves by showing the Señora de Bringas all their dress materials and other articles of wear. "This will be worn a great deal in the autumn ... We have a large assortment of these because they are going to be all the rage this season." The phrases seemed to come out of the folds of cloth as the bolts were unrolled. The proprietor, just getting ready for his usual summer trip to Paris, sometimes urged her to buy something particularly attractive, and she occasionally fell into temptation, either because the things really were bargains, or because their fine quality struck her in the eye and lit the fires of her passion for materials, and she could hardly help satisfying her desire, even under pain of suffering for it later on.

Oh, when autumn came she would make up to herself for the martyrdom of that summer by dressing as she ought to dress. She was going to make herself a velvet costume for the winter and a bonnet to go with it, both in the most striking, new, and elegant style. And she would dress her children like princes and princesses. That stupid man should find with whom he had to deal. Revolving in her mind these plans and others of the same nature, she would walk slowly along through the streets on her way back home again, sometimes stopping before the windows of modistes' and jewellers' shops and making calculations of the more or less remote possibilities of ever possessing the handsome and expensive things she saw in them.

The sadness of Madrid at that season of the year increased her own sadness. The empty silence of many of the streets at the hottest hours and the melancholy cries of the vendors of *horchata* and lemonade, the slow walk of the jaded horses, the shop doors covered with their long shrouds, are more designed to lower the spirits than to raise them, especially when they are combined with the effects of a very high temperature on the skin and a nostalgia for sea beaches. Those summer storms accompanied by gusts of wind full of dirty dust got badly on her nerves too, and the only satisfaction that she derived from them was seeing them give the lie to her husband's meteorological prognostications. For whenever the sky clouded over Bringas would say: "You'll see how cool it will be this afternoon." How cool indeed! It was always twice as hot as it had been before!

On the rare occasions when she went out at night, the stifling heat of the early evening hours depressed her horribly, especially when she thought of those happy

213

beings who at that very moment were strolling about in *La Zurriola*. Madrid seemed commonplace and dingy to her, like a large village full of dirty and uncivilised people.

When she looked at the inhabitants of the poorer quarters, who lived almost entirely on the sidewalks—the men in shirt sleeves and the women in their lightest clothes, while the children played half naked in the gutters—she fancied herself among the Moors—for that was her idea of what the cities of Africa were like. She herself always rose early and took a bath at home, since she would not lower herself to being the Naiad of a river as vulgar and unfashionable as the Manzanares. In those first hours of the day, with the balcony windows on the West half open, there was a slight coolness in the air, and her spirit as well as her body felt refreshed.

When she made her round of the shops she was repelled by the smells that drifted out of the doorways in the more densely populated streets, an odour of humanity and cooking food. Sometimes there was a breath of cooler air from these basement windows but it was generally accompanied by such a repugnant smell that it made her hurry on towards the river bank. There the sight of the water flowing along the irrigation canals gave her a feeling of pleasure, and she could almost have wished to receive the stream on her own skin. But such an asphyxiating smell rose from the wet soil, a mixture of all sorts of horrid emanations, that she was obliged to hurry on again. The dogs drank from the dirty pool left behind by the irrigation water and then went to lie down again in the shade, where they joined the ambulant street vendors who were tired of crying their goat-skin slippers and lamp chimneys, *all at a real*, nails, railway guides, tin whistles, and enamel *cooking pots to save charcoal*. At hours like these and in that horrible season only Bringas and the flies were happy.

214

XXXVI

I think it was on San Lorenzo's Day that Bringas and his wife received a letter that puzzled and perplexed them both. This extraordinary missive which surprised our friends in their solitude was from Augustin Caballero; and it seemed to both of them as if the phantasm of their generous cousin was standing before them. Expressing itself in the plural, the letter said that *they* had taken a house in Arcachon and, feeling sure that Bringas and the children needed sea air, they invited the whole family to come and spend a month there with them. The invitation was both cordial and explicit. The house was very large, with every comfort, and the Bringas family would be received as honoured guests and treated like royalty, without having expenses of any kind. "Amparo and I," the letter concluded, "will be extremely happy if you can come."

Rosalía's first feeling was one of anger and scorn. How did they dare to invite an honourable family to stay with them? "It's to try to improve their position by having us under their roof. It's so that they can pretend to be decent people by appearing with us in public ... In a word we are to be the flag under which they'll pass the contraband. Doesn't it make you furious? Really it's an insult."

But Don Francisco was so busily employed in trying to sort out the confusion of ideas that the letter had left in his mind that he had no time to get indignant. So his wife continued to ruminate her scorn alone; and, as she did so, brilliant lightning flashes began to appear in the storm clouds that had gathered in her brain, flashes which spelled out the name *Arcachon*. In the round rich sound of this word (more attractive if pronounced in a nasal tone) was contained a whole world of elegant satisfactions for Rosalía. To be on her way to France and to meet Spanish families she knew in the stations at San Sebastian and Saint Jean de Luz, and to be able to say to them casually when the first greetings were over: "We are going to Arcachon," would be like being able to claim relationship with God the Father. At the very thought of it a gust of incense-breathing smoke seemed to rise from her heart and fill her thorax and go on to her nose, making it prickle and dilate.

After much labour the mind of Bringas finally brought forth this idea which took the form of a question:

"Do you suppose they are married?"

"Married? Of course not! They would have boasted of it if they were. No, they are still living together like animals, and it's disgraceful that they should ask us to stay with them when they are living like that. They must think we are no better than they are!"

"What a pity they aren't married!" Bringas murmured, gazing down sadly. "Because if they were living together as God ordains ... It's really such an opportunity. Free tickets, our board and lodging, everything free."

But the idea of having to humiliate herself to Amparo by being her guest and accepting such a great favour from her, roused Rosalía's pride.

"You mean you would be willing to accept this invitation," she said. "I couldn't lower myself to do it."

"No, no, that is to say ... I was only thinking," Bringas stammered, more perplexed than ever. "But after all, we have no reason to suppose that they haven't got married by this time."

"Whether they are married or not—do you think it would be right for us to go? To visit this silly creature to

216

whom we used to give the scraps left over from our table!"

"My dear, don't be so proud. Who remembers anything about that now? The world soon forgets such things. If people have money, no one is going to ask them where they used to get free meals. And remember that in Arcachon no one is going to know any of us. It's not that I want to go—I'd far rather not go away at all. I'll reply thanking them very much . . ."

But this absolute negative again threw into relief for the lady the ideal perspective of a trip to the famous summer resort Arcachon. In the visits she would pay that autumn how musically and deliciously the phrase would sound, a phrase so purely aristocratic that it suggested the rustling of silk: "We have been in Arcachon." The spark was enough to make the storm break again in that haughty mind. And meanwhile the brain of Bringas was seething with financial considerations, such as: 'What an opportunity to have a holiday in France without spending a real!'

The husband and wife sat for a long time without exchanging a word, each contemplating and turning over their different ideas. At times they looked at each other in silence. No doubt each hoped that the other would break the silence first and propose some formula of conciliation. That evening they discussed the invitation again, but Rosalía was still firmly entrenched in her pride and persisted in declaring her repugnance to the idea and her low opinion of Augustin and Amparo. That night, however, the idea of the journey presented itself in such glowing colours that she ventured to ask herself a question which was inspired by a consideration of the real nature of things: "And what does it matter to me," she thought, "if they are married or not, or *what* she is?" And her soul became filled with tolerance.

Still she did not want to yield too easily, so she waited for her husband to make the first move so that she could have the satisfaction of appearing to give in only through obedience and resignation. Meanwhile Don Francisco, who had been carefully weighing the advantages and disadvantages of the journey in his mind, kept looking at his wife as if he wanted her to take the initiative. It was like one of those occasions when two people have been quarrelling, and neither wants to be the one to break the ice and make a move towards peace.

Rosalía went to bed sure that the next morning Bringas would express himself as being in favour of accepting their cousin's invitation. She had already decided what she was going to say. First she would be angry and stand upon her dignity, and then have much to say against Amparo and Augustin; afterwards there would be a series of modulations into another key—such as that she was accustomed to never thinking of herself and to sacrificing her wishes to those of the rest. For her children's sake she was prepared to make any sacrifice and even to suffer slights and humiliations. It was obvious that Isabelita needed sea bathing, and it would be good for Alfonsito too; and confronted with an opportunity of getting this benefit for her children, her own desires and even her scruples were of no account. In fact, if Bringas thought that they ought to go, she would close her eyes to everything and . . ."

But contrary to her expectations her husband did not say a word about the trip next morning. He got up rather late, and seemed to have forgotten all about it. In vain Rosalía tried to prick him, saying how horrible the baths of the *Jeronimos* were, and complaining of the dreadful heat. He only said:

"Well, it's almost over now. After the 15th, it will begin to get cooler."

Rosalía began to despair. She waited until the afternoon; and then finding that the Palace Mouse still did not say anything about Arcachon, she ventured to remark:

"What reply are you going to make to Augustin? As far as I am concerned, though it's repugnant to me to think of staying with such people, still for the sake of the children ..."

"For the sake of what children?" Bringas exclaimed. "Why the children simply couldn't be better!"

And he waved his straw hat about his head as if he were giving a cheer.

"I tell you the baths of the Manzanares are the best in the world! Look what a colour Isabelita has! And Alfonsin is as strong as an oak. I laugh whenever I think of those idiots who go abroad in summer ... And, you know, last night I was thinking it all over and, say what you will, there are bound to be expenses. We will have free tickets to the border, yes, but what about the trip from the border to Arcachon?"

"But it's only two hundred and thirty kilometres on," Rosalía said with surprising spontaneity. She had been feeding her dreams by reading the railway guide.

"Whether they are few or many, those kilometres are sure to turn out expensive. And there's another thing— we can't go to see them without taking them a handsome present. Do you think it would look well to arrive with empty hands? And there are sure to be other expenses. So I say definitely that we aren't going. After the 15th it will begin to get cooler. You can notice a change already, last night the temperature was certainly lower. No, we won't go anywhere, my dear, we are getting along very well here in Madrid."

Rosalía listened to her husband's remarks with acute annoyance, but her pride prevented her from contradicting him, and she was silent. Only in her breast the

219

sparks of her extinguished illusions writhed and twisted. She had already got so accustomed to the idea of meeting her friends in the station at San Sebastian and throwing Arcachon in their teeth, to the idea of putting Arcachon at the head of her letters, and in short, of Arcachonizing herself for the whole of the coming autumn and winter, that the abandonment of the project was painful.

XXXVII

In her sad, exiled state the only thing that gave Rosalía real pleasure was that her children had never before been in such good health. Isabelita's attacks were always a cause of great anxiety to her mother, but that summer the child did not have a single one of those convulsive fits which were spoiling her childhood. Whether the baths in the river were really doing her good or not, the fact is that the little girl had improved enormously since she had begun to take them. She had put on flesh and had a good colour and an excellent appetite. As for Alfonsin— since he had been trying the waters of the Manzanares he was almost bursting with health. He was so strong that he could not stop trying his strength out, and straining to develop himself and become even larger and stronger. This instinct of growth drove him to incessant activity and to all sorts of acts that required strength and energy. To climb the highest places he could get at, to crawl along ledges, to jump about, to carry weights, to drag furniture around, to turn things over and splash water, to play with fire (and with gunpowder if he could only have got hold of some)—these were his greatest diversions. He showed none of his father's mechanical skill, but on the contrary a precocious talent for destroying everything he could get his hands on. During these trials of strength he made use of all sorts of courses and bad words which he picked up in the Palace streets upstairs. When his squeamish little sister heard him she was off at once to carry tales to his father.

"Papa, Alfonsito is saying such things . . ."

And Don Francisco, who abhorred bad language, would shout to him.

"Child, come here at once. Somebody bring me a chile pepper from the kitchen."

Then, with the pepper in one hand and the criminal held firmly by the neck, he would pretend that he was going to scrub out his mouth with the pepper. Then he would frown and say:

"This time I will let you off. But if you keep on saying those dirty words, I'll burn your mouth with the pepper, and then your tongue will fall out, and instead of talking as people do, you'll bray like a donkey."

Alfonso had a passion for the big furniture vans. To see one in the streets was his greatest delight. Everything about them filled him with enthusiasm—the powerful horses, that huge box in which all the household goods were stored, the mirrors and cooking pots fastened on below, and most all the big chaps in blue blouses sitting on top of the wagon and nodding in time to its slow motion. His dream was to be one of those big chaps, and drive a wagon like that, and load and unload it; and he imagined one that was so big that it would hold all the furniture in the Palace. In his attempt to use his imagination and his muscles at the same time he imitated grown up life as well as he could. As Don Quixote dreamed adventures and tried to make them come true, so Alfonsin imagined extraordinary house-movings and tried to realise them in his own way.

One afternoon, when Don Francisco was sitting in *Gasperini* with Isabelita, he heard a loud noise of furniture being moved, cracks of a whip and shouts of: "Whoa Arré! Gee up!" Alfonsin had piled up all the chairs in the middle of the room, and between their legs had put cooking pots, the pestle and mortar, bundles of cloth, brooms, and anything else he could lay hands on. Then he had begun to lash at the pile with his whip, and if anything fell down there were shouts and kicks and curses. He had a perfectly crimson face and was perspiring freely by the time Isabelita appeared, sent in by her father to find out what in the world the noise was.

"If only you could see him, Papa," the little girl reported when she came back, almost dying with laughter. "He has got all the chairs piled up on top of each other, and he is whipping them and saying such silly things . . ."

"Go and tell that little brute from me that if I have to come in there to him, I'll make his behind as red as a tomato . . ."

Isabelita's tastes and inclinations were entirely different from her brother's. It was in fact not so much a difference of age and sex which made the two children generally play apart as one of temperament. Isabelita, though she sometimes played with dolls, did not take so much pleasure in these games as she did in gathering and keeping all sorts of little things. She had the true collector's mania; useless trash gravitated to her hands, and any object which was wandering about the house without an owner, ended up in one of the boxes which she kept in a corner at the foot of her bed. And no one must touch this sacred deposit! If Alfonsin managed to get his profane hands on it, the little girl would complain about it for weeks afterwards.

These magpie habits increased when the child's health grew worse; then the only thing she seemed to enjoy was turning over her treasure and rearranging the objects that composed it. They were of the most extraordinary diversity, and in general of the most absolute uselessness. Pieces of embroidery and bits of silk and woollen cloth filled one large box; buttons, labels from empty perfume bottles, bands from cigars, used postage stamps, worn cut steel pens and empty match boxes filled another; while the number of formless things, fragments of no possible use or application, approached the incalcul-

able. But her favourite box contained those French religious prints, which were given as prizes at her school,
chromos of the Sacred Heart, *Amor Hermoso*, Maria Alcoque
and Bernadette—little pictures in which the art of Paris
represents the holy things in the style of fashion plates.
Then there was a collection of what the child called
embroidered paper, by which she meant the stamped
leaves of paper that come in tabacco boxes. And there
was positively no counting the papers of needles with no
needles in them, the artificial flowers, the small figures
left over from Christmas crèches, and the thousands of
other little objects stored away in the child's boxes.

Isabelita kept her money carefully secreted in another
place. When the money box was shaken, it gave out a
delicious music of chiming pennies. It was so full that it
weighed pounds and pounds. It cost the poor child a
great deal of trouble to watch over it and hide it from
Alfonsin's greedy hands; for if he had once got hold of
it, he would have broken it to get the money out and then
spent it all on trifles—or on a moving van with real horses!

The little girl was so enamoured of this treasure of
odds and ends that she hid it from everybody, even from
her beloved Mama. This was because her mother dis-
arranged it when she looked at it and spoiled the order
it was in; and then she seemed to regard it as being of
little value, sometimes even saying:

"Don't be miserly, child. What pleasure can you get
from keeping such trash?"

The only person in fact whom Isabelita would allow
to touch her treasure was her father, and that was because
he admired the little girl's patience and praised her habit
of keeping things. On those long summer days when Don
Francisco could neither read nor work nor occupy himself in anything that interested him, he would have been
bored to death if he had not found a resource in playing

with his little daughter and helping her to arrange and rearrange her small possessions.

"Angel," he would say, when he got up after taking his siesta, "bring your boxes here and we'll amuse ourselves with them."

And the two of them alone in *Gasperini* would pass whole afternoons sitting on the floor, taking out objects and classifying them and then putting them back again.

"Some of these things will come in for something yet," the great economist would say. "Let's put the apricot stones together here ... I'll count them: twenty-three. Then we'll put the pen box with the beads here so the apricot stones can't roll. Now let's cover them all with this piece of paper to keep them in place. The broken bits of pottery better come next, and then the bone buttons—we'll separate them from the wooden ones so they won't quarrel. And the works of art should have a box of their own—it will be the Museum to which the English will come ... Where are the whistles? Keep on handing me things."

And while Isabelita played so quietly with her father in *Gasperini*, that brute of an Alfonsin would be in the next room, shouting at his team and pilling up his wagon. In all difficulties the little boy sought refuge behind his mother's skirts, while the little girl generally went to her father to get justice in her disputes with her small brother. Alfonsito knew only too well how to get round his mother when he wanted pennies. He would climb up in her lap and put his arms about her neck and whisper in her ear:

"A secret, Mama, a secret—"

"I know what your secret is! My angel wants a penny, isn't that it?"

But one day the little wretch whispered in her ear instead:

"Papa says I take after you, I'm a crazy boy."

XXXVIII

Rosalía watched the days pass by in the second half of August with something approaching real terror; for according to all calculations, they are followed by the first days of September. A suggestion she made to Torres about a possible extension of time made him turn pale. He said that Torquemada could not possibly wait for his money. All sorts of reasons made it impossible; they had both made this clear to her on the day the contract was signed. It was the principal clause in that document, and the Señor de Torquemada had counted on her exact carrying out of the agreement.

And, as she listened, the Señora de Bringas began to suspect that the difficulties confronting her this time were much more serious than they had been on previous occasions. It is unnecessary to state—since certain things speak for themselves—that Milagros' majordomo had not brought the promised money, either on the 4th or the 5th or on any other day in August. There was no use looking for anything from Cándida but airy fantasies. To whom could she turn? Bringas would soon be quite well: it would be madness to try to take money out of the domestic treasury again. It might be best simply to confess her weakness frankly to her husband; but it was also the most difficult course to take. What a state he would be in! People would hire balconies to hear him! If Bringas discovered her deception a period of strong repression would set in which would be more painful for Rosalía than all the difficulties she had passed through. Her plan was to emancipate herself gradually, and on no account to become more strongly bound by authority than before. No, she would somehow manage to get through her troubles by herself, with the aid of Providence. God would not abandon her, he had never done so on previous occasions.

After the 25th she began to notice in herself an anxious, feverish feeling and her lips seemed always to be tasting something bitter. The thought of her situation never left her a moment's peace, and the worst of it was that she could not think of any possible solution. If Pez would only come back! He had offered to help her so many times. Yet when she remembered how harsh she had been with him before he left, she wondered whether he would be in the same mind when he returned to Madrid. But then she thought to herself: "He is mad about me. I can do what I like with him." And she recalled that burning day when he had shown himself so amorous and accused herself of excessive prudery. If she had not been so silly then, she need never have had to beg for money from that kaffir Torquemada. For a woman of her distinction to undergo such agonies—and for such a small sum—when she might have had thousands of duros if she had cared to! Eight years before the Marques de Fucar had paid court to her at Milagros' *tertulias*. And she? A porcupine! And the Marques was by no means her only admirer. Plenty of other men, and all of them wealthy too, had shown by their insistent gallantry that they were ready to commit any folly for her sake. But she had always remained inflexible in her cold pride and honour, and had never suspected that this inflexibility which had seemed then as high and strong as a tower would one day feel itself trembling to the foundations. But what she had felt in those earlier days had become so alien to her now that she hardly seemed to herself to be the same person.

"Necessity is what creates character," she said to herself.

She had to blame herself for so many things that she ought not to have done and when she remembered this, she felt that she should be more indulgent to people who do not keep all the Ten Commandments. Before we blame them, we ought to say to them: 'Take what money you need; buy yourself something to eat, and clothes to cover your body. Have you had enough to eat? Are you properly dressed? Well then, it's time to talk about morality now.'

When such thoughts came to her, Rosalía wondered at herself; that is, she wondered at the Rosalía of the earlier epoch before she began to be involved in these frauds and deceptions which kept her in such a state of apprehension and anxiety. And if she could not recall without a blush how unfashionable she had been in those days, she was still proud to remember how honourable she had always been and how patiently she had accepted her hard life. The castle of her simple happiness was still standing, but the mine which was to blow it up was already laid. And before setting off the fuse, while she was still unstained in deed at least, she paused to gaze sadly at the edifice, so that she would remember it well in the days to come when she would be seated on its ruins.

On those last nights of August she went to the Prado several times to join the Cucurbitases there. And though she was tormented by a feeling of imminent disaster, she managed to play her part in the light conversation of the *tertulia*. It was an animated group and contained several gentlemen; and the Señora de Bringas could not help mentally passing these in review and assessing their possibilities as aids and providers.

"This one," she thought, "is even poorer than we are. He's all façade and show—and underneath that tinsel a wretched salary of twenty thousand reals. I don't know how they manage to keep that big family on it ... And this one has nothing but debts and a lot of fine talk ...

Ah, here is a man who is different. He is supposed to have an income of twelve thousand duros. But they say he isn't interested in women ... This one certainly shows every sign of liking women, but he expects them to keep him—and how conceited he is! ... Here's another who hasn't a penny to bless himself with, and he's a vulgar libertine, too, who only has affairs with women of bad character ... Now here's a man who really seems to be very much attracted to me; but I know through Torres that he had to borrow two thousand reals to take his wife to the baths, because she is crippled with rheumatism, poor thing."

At the end of this review of masculine possibilities, it appeared that almost all the men present were more or less poverty-stricken creatures, hiding their indigence under frock coats bought with infinite difficulty; while the few who really were well off seemed to have cold and cautious temperaments. It seemed to the lady as if she were enclosed inside two unbreakable walls, poverty being one and honour the other. If she sprang over them what would she find on the other side?

As she sat in the semi-obscurity of the Prado and watched the dizzying procession of passers-by, she saw among them various men whom she knew to be rich and who consequently drew her attention. The street lantern nearest the place where they were sitting lighted these passing forms sufficiently for her recognize them as they went past, and then they were lost again in the dusty shadows. Thus she saw the Marques de Fucar, recently returned, she knew, from Biarritz, plump, pompous and simply padded with bank notes; and then Trujillo the banker, and then Mompous, the stock exchange broker and Don Buenaventura de Lantigua and others of the same sort. Among these powerful personages there were some whom she knew personally and others whom she only knew by sight; some of them had given her what seemed to be amorous glances, while others were said to be of impeccable behaviour both at home and abroad.

Rosalía went home with her head full of these Madrid magnates, and their figures kept moving through her mind, coming and going there as they had passed and repassed in the Prado. As if to reproach her for these thoughts, Bringas was particularly kind and affectionate that night, though in anything to do with money he was more inflexible than ever.

"My dear," he said, when they were going to bed, "I shall be going back to the office on the first of September and then we must get down to work again, and above all we must try to spend as little money as possible. We have got behindhand, and we must try hard to regain the lost ground by means of strict economy. I count on you now, as I have always counted on you. I depend on your carefulness, your obedience and your good sense. If we are to get ahead again, we must not spend even a real on unnecessary things for at least a year. With the clothes you have now, you can be elegant for six years at least—and if you will sell something you don't need so that I can get myself a new suit, these poor bones will bless you. Forgive me if I have been severe sometimes. It seemed to me that you were acquiring certain bad habits and getting out of line with our traditional regime. But when I take into consideration all your virtues, I can easily overlook that ostentation you sometimes show. And I hope that in return you will gratify me by returning to our quiet ways, and not force me to lay down the law. If we each do our part our children will have enough to eat and clothes to their backs, and I can await the coming of old age in peace and tranquility."

Rosalía was touched by these reasonable though severe arguments, but she was frightened too. For she felt that she could not return to the old system of *One dress behind you and the other still to come,* and the infinite metamorphoses of the peach-coloured costume. And yet the thought of deceiving her unfortunate husband was very painful to her. In her perplexity she decided to leave everything to chance or Providence, saying to herself: "God will aid me. What I do must depend on circumstances." If only the great Pez would return soon, he would resolve all her doubts and uncertainties. And she would think of some way of exploiting his generosity without selling herself, though if she managed to do that she would be the cleverest woman in the world. But Don Manuel would first have to return from those wretched baths. Carolina said that he was coming back in the beginning of September, but that he hadn't fixed a date yet. And on the 2nd—.

The absolutely essential thing, the Señora de Bringas realised, was to stop the money-lender from coming down on her with his demand for payment, or at any rate to delay it for a few days until Pez had got back. In spite of Torres' pessimistic opinion she still hoped that she might produce some effect on Torquemada by going to see him herself. So on the 31st she ventured to go to his house; it was a very disagreeable step to have to take, but she placed much dependence on it.

The money-lender lived in the Calle de Moriana in a big room, dark, dusty and packed with odd pieces of furniture and large pictures—spoils garnered from his enormous clientèle. It was a museum of the craving for impossible luxury, of foolish wastefulness and brief splendours: a repository of tears and regrets. Rosalía felt a secret terror as she entered it; and when Torquemada appeared, emerging from between these melancholy objects, wearing a Turkish cap and a gray velveteen jacket, she wanted to weep.

231

XXXIX

"And how is the family?" the money lender asked, after he had greeted Rosalía.

"They are all in their usual health, thank you," she answered, sitting down on the chair he offered her.

And she began at once to explain her need for an extension of time, stating her request in the nicest way she could, and using her most amiable smiles. But Torquemada listened to her coldly and seriously, and then, offering her the doughnut formed by his fingers to gaze at, as the Host is offered to the adoration of the faithful, he pronounced these fatal words:

"Señora, I have already explained to you that I can . . . not, cannot possibly do it. It is quite im . . . possible."

And seeing that his victim still refused to believe that he could be so cruel, he threw in his last argument:

"If my father asked for this . . . extension of time, I would not let him have it. You don't know what difficulties I am in. I absolutely must make . . . a payment. My honour is involved."

And though she repeated her supplications to the point of tediousness, they did not touch that heart of stone.

"Only ten days—" she said; the bond seemed to be sticking in her throat.

"Not even ten minutes, Señora. I really . . . cannot do it. I am very sorry, but if by the 2nd—"

"For Gods's sake, by the memory of your mother!"

"I shall be obliged to take the agreement to the Señor de Bringas, who, I am told, is a man of means . . ."

In spite of this cold determined negative, the poor lady, after passing a sleepless night in a state of intense anxiety, returned to see the money-lender again on the following day.

"And the family?" he asked as usual, after the first greetings.

Rosalía made her supplication again with even more fervour than she had done the day before. And Torquemada refused and refused over and over, continually accenting his cruelty with the alarming apparition of the doughnut set in the space where the eyes of the two speakers met. In the end Rosalía entrusted to tears what she had not been able to obtain with sighs. The money-lender thought that she was going to faint and sent for a glass cf water, but the poor lady could not bring herself to drink it. The power of a woman's tears was proved once more on this occasion, for even the stony Torquemada grew soft in the end, and the extension of time was finally granted.

"But I swear to you, Señora, that if on the 7th—"

"The 7th? Oh, no, the 10th!"

The 8th, then—No, that won't do, the 8th is a holiday, the Virgin of—Well, the Virgin of . . . September. But to show that I want to do all I can to help you, I will make it the 9th. But if on the 9th you still aren't able to pay me what you owe me, I shall feel myself obliged . . . The Señor de Bringas would certainly have the money."

"Oh, thank God, until the 10th!"

Rosalía considered herself extremely fortunate to have gained these few days of grace. At any moment Pez might arrive. Please God he would come soon.

At the beginning of September Bringas began to go to the office again, though he did very little work and spent most of his time talking to the second-in-command. It was a scandal that they had cut down his salary for the month of August; and when *La Señora* came back he meant to secure her interest to have this graceless blunder corrected.

233

While Bringas was at the office his wife spent most of her time alone. She had few visitors because most of her friends were still away at bathing places. Refugio came to see her two or three times to talk about the styles and about the luxurious articles of dress she was receiving from Burgos. Rosalía was no longer so haughty to her, though she was always careful to show her sense of the difference between a respectable married lady and a woman of mysterious and equivocal conduct.

Since she had got herself into these financial quicksands, the Señora de Bringas had acquired a habit of looking at everyone she met and trying to calculate how much money they might have to dispose of. And one day when the Sánchez girl was with her, talking about the business she was setting up in very opulent sounding terms, Rosalía said to herself:

"That she-dog has money."

And, when she was leaving, Rosalía actually had the daring thought of asking her for a loan. But how horrible! She drove the ignominious thought from her mind as quickly as she could. No, before she would humiliate herself like that, she would go to her husband and tell him her terrible story, and let him say what he would. Refugio was a bad lot. Rosalía blushed to think that she had ever even thought of lowering herself to beg such favours. Only the day before Torres had been telling her that that prosperous looking young woman was the scandal of the neighbourhood she lived in, and was having affairs with three or four men at the same time.

On the 5th of September one of the shop assistants from *Sobrino Hermanos* brought her a message from the proprietor. It was to the effect that the new autumn styles were arriving from Paris and were really wonderful, and Sobrino would like to show them to his distinguished customer himself and get her opinion on some of the materials, which he felt were perhaps almost too striking in colour and design. She went of course. But all the new and beautiful things she looked at could not draw her out of her deep melancholy. She wanted to buy everything—or at any rate something. But how could she do it when she was in such a desperate situation, and menaced by a domestic cataclysm?

"I brought this back especially for you!" Sobrino kept saying with Mephistophelean amiability.

But she put on a disconsolate expression, complaining that she had a bad headache, and refused to buy anything, though she could hardly take her eyes off the new materials and was even more deeply stirred by the beauty of the wonderful model gowns displayed on the wax figures. As for the *fichus*, the embroideries, the cloaks, the blouses, the pelisses—it was an Arabian Nights' Entertainment of dress.

The next day was the 6th, and Rosalía felt the garrotte around her neck already. If she went to *Sobrino Hermanos* again, it was only to distract herself, and to try to drive the terrible image of Torquemada out of her mind for a little while. But as she was on her way there, passing through the Calle del Arenal, she met Joaquinito Pez, who said to her in a joyful tone:

"We've just had a letter from Papa; they are on their way back."

For Rosalía to hear this and to see the skies opening, the problem of the 9th resolved, the world a better place, and humanity redeemed from its ancient sorrows, was all one. She continued along the street at a quicker pace, her fresh fair face scattering happiness as she went. And when she got to Sobrino's, she began to look at all the new things again, and give her opinion on them, praising some and condemning others, tireless in looking and commenting.

"Have this sent home for me please. You see, Señor Sobrino, you are having your way in the end, I am going to get this *fichu*."

These and similar phrases, all referring to purchases, embellished the stream of her animated conversation that day.

XL

The great man arrived. Rosalía was convinced that the first visit he would pay, after he had washed off the dust of the journey, would be to his friends in the Palace; so as soon as Bringas had gone to the office, she began to dress herself with great care to be ready to receive this being who had filled her thoughts in her saddest hours. Because Don Manuel would surely return from the baths more vigorous, more chivalrous and more generous than he had been before—and that was saying much. She recognized his footsteps as they drew near the door, and was suddenly overcome by a feeling of shyness. But how absurd! She gave her figure one last glance in the mirror and saw that she had never looked handsomer; then, after making him wait a few minutes, she went in to the drawing room, where Prudencia had put him. Her emotion was so strong when she greeted him that it made her slightly awkward, and she was aware that she was contradicting herself as she answered his questions about Don Francisco's recovery.

How well he looked! He seemed to have left ten years behind him and returned to his best days. But though he was as amiable and well bred as ever, Rosalía noticed something immediately which seemed to her both strange and discouraging.

She had imagined that from the very first moment he appeared Pez would show himself as ardent as he had been before he left Madrid; but she had been completely mistaken in this idea. Pez was calm and reserved, and only showed her the usual polite attentions which he would have shown to any lady of his acquaintance. Was it

237

because his feelings for her had entirely changed? It was certainly not because she did not look her best that day, for she was wonderfully handsome. Time passed, and Rosalía could not recover from her astonishment, which gradually turned into indignation as Pez exhausted all the usual commonplace subjects of conversation—the weather, the heat in Madrid, the health of their families and friends, the political conspiracies—without once touching on the subject which, to the lady, seemed far more opportune. The briefness of her replies, and the nervous emphasis with which she fanned herself, were outward indications of her annoyance; while Pez seemed to grow cooler all the time, and talked on indifferent subjects, with an irritating air of being a superior person above human miseries, and without showing the least sign of being enchanted, or saying anything that suggested a vacillating conscience or a virtue in danger.

Had the Northern air turned him into an exemplary character, a model of right thinking and temperance? That likeness to the Holy Patriarch had never struck Rosalía so strongly before; and at that moment she thought his blond good looks the most insipid type of human perfection in the world. He only needed that spray of lilies to be able walk straight into one of those coloured prints they sell for a peseta in the streets. She began to be disgusted by this circumspection, and was collecting all her contempt to give it whole hearted expression, when the idea of that payment that must be made on the 9th suddenly struck her with overwhelming force. Her face changed: Pez read something in it and said to her:

"You are pale."

Rosalía did not answer. For the moment she was dazed with misery, thinking to herself: 'When you speak of sin, call it necessity and you will have spoken the truest word in the world. For what woman, if she were not in desperate need, would be such a fool as to be taken in by these *canailles* of men.'

Pez, when she remained silent, became a little more tender in his manner, and said that he had noticed that she did not seem quite herself; she was melancholy perhaps, or had some serious preoccupation. She felt that this was an opportunity to find out if Pez was still the same ardent and generous-minded person he had been before, or if he had changed into a thick-skinned egotist; so she answered, with an appearance of graceful reserve:

"Oh, secrets of mine. Who would be interested in them but me?"

Slowly Pez descended from those heights of virtue to which he had climbed. He leaned towards the lady, spoke of ingratitude in tones of amorous complaint. Rosalía glimpsed bright horizons of salvation, lighting with their far-off ray the darkness of that fatal 9th, now looming so close. But unfortunately just then there was a sudden knocking at the door and the children came in, and Rosalía could not be more explicit. She only found time to say:

"I have been wanting you to come back. I must talk to you."

The children's kisses interrupted this interesting conference, which had finally begun to go according to the lady's plans. But later on, after Bringas had returned and had had a long conversation with Pez on political themes, Rosalía found an opportunity to talk to her friend alone for some time, until Pez finally ended his visit and went away.

The daughter of the Pipaóns was sad rather than happy for the rest of that evening and night. Her husband noticed an unusual tendency to silence in her; she was indeed almost completely mute. But, according to his

239

custom on such occasions, he made no effort to change her state. Silence is better than loquacity in a woman, they say, and Bringas had no desire to go against this rule.

On the morning of the 8th, Rosalía dressed herself very neatly, but simply, and said goodbye to her husband. She was going to hear mass, as could be seen by the missal with its mother of pearl clasps which she was carrying. Her husband was not to wait dinner if she was late, because she was going to visit the Señorita de Cucurbitas who was dangerously ill.

"I heard that they were going to give her the Last Sacraments today," Bringas said, with real pain.

Rosalía went out, after giving Prudencia orders about dinner in case she should be late in coming in, and Don Francisco remained behind in the hands of the barber, for since his illness he had been afraid to try to shave himself. Paquito was sitting with him, and the father was finding fault with the son in a friendly way. For the boy had not been able to hold out against the influence which expansive ideas always have upon youth. He had let himself be contaminated in the University by germs of sympathy for the *so-called* Revolution. Among his companions the standard of Liberalism was freely waving on high, but though Paquito had not yet reached that point, he had developed reservations in his ways of thought, weaknesses; in fact the boy was definitely infected by the virus.

"You must get rid of these revolutionary ideas—" Bringas kept saying to his son while the barber was shaving him. "You will see what will happen if these *canailles* succeed. The horrors of the French Revolution will be nothing to the tragedies which will be enacted here."

Another mania with which the boy was poisoning his mind, and which infuriated Don Francisco, was a perverse doctrine known as Krausism. Bringas had heard it described as pestilential by a learned chaplain of his acquaintance. For some time Paquito had been babbling about the I and the *Not* I, and the other, and the one further off, until he had nearly driven his father crazy. Don Francisco had finally told his son in so many words that, if he didn't forget all about these new-fangle philosophies, he would take him away from the University and put him in a shop as a clerk.

The morning passed, and Rosalía did not return, so they finally had their dinner. Not long after she came in, rather out of breath.

"The poor thing is very ill," she said, forestalling her husband, whose mouth was already opening to ask after Cucurbitas' sister.

And she went to the *Camón* to take off her veil and put on another dress.

That evening they all went for a walk in the park, dressed in their Sunday clothes and on their best behaviour,—the children walking quietly in front and the mother and father following them, calm and dignified as usual. The daughter of the Pipaón de la Barcas had never regarded her husband with more respect than she did that day. She looked at him almost with veneration, and thought of herself as extraordinarily inferior to him, so inferior that she was hardly worthy even to lift her eyes to him. Her mind was far away from these simple domestic scenes, and scarcely took in what was being done and said around her. She was living in some different region, attentive to things unknown to the others.

"But you are in some other world tonight!" Bringas said, getting rather annoyed with her at last when she had answered him at random three of four times. But she made no reply. Afterwards, when they had returned

241

home and the father and children were playing at lottery, she shut herself up in the *Camón*. And there, sitting with her arms folded and her head sunk on her breast, she abandoned herself to the reflections which were preying on her mind like fire in stubble.

XLI

"His expression! Though he tried hard to conceal his feelings, I could see how badly he took it ... 'This trip has ruined me ... The girls bought everything they saw in Bayonne, I spent my whole year's salary ... Still, I'll try to do something, we must see, I'll look around ..., Oh, Holy Virgin, it's a fearful thing to sell oneself and not even to be paid! ... But surely he will do everything he can, so as not to lose face in front of me. He said that he would send me a letter at ten o'clock tomorrow— Surely he will do everything possible before letting himself look ridiculous! If he hasn't got the money he must get it somewhere. It is his duty. How much more than that I am worth, how much more! I am giving a treasure for a pittance. What am I asking compared to some women who have eaten up whole fortunes? It is a disgrace to have to speak of such a small sum to a gentleman ... I am tasting all the bitterness a mouth can taste ..."

She passed the night in a state of wretched uncertainty, continually waked by the sharp pricking of her fixed idea, which would not let her sleep. Beside her Don Francisco slept like a labourer who has worked hard all day and who, as soon as he closes his eyes, lays down all the burdens on his spirit too. Fortunate man! He needed nothing for himself and was happy in his old nankeen suit. He never wanted anything better than his cheap unstylish cravat, the kind the street vendors sell at the corner of the Post Office. *Tell me your needs and I'll tell you if you're honourable.* This proverb suddenly ran through Rosalía's mind, without her realising that she was a mistress of popular philosophy.

"After all, what were the Saints?" she thought. "People who didn't mind going out into the streets looking like scarecrows. I haven't got that indifference to appearances which is the basis of virtue. Saints are born not made. You can't acquire merits by will; you have to bring them with you from the other world. My husband was born caring nothing about fashion, and he will die in the odour of sanctity."

But these reflections did not keep her from envying him, now that she was finding out by experience how dearly you can pay for wanting to be in the fashion. The poor woman saw herself surrounded by dangers and was full of anxieties and regrets; while her husband was sleeping tranquilly on the edge of the abyss.

For he slept as if he were far away from the shame that was really so close beside him. And for all that that vain creature, his wife, could do to appease her conscience with sophisms, that conscience would not be quieted and soon became restless again. But Rosalía could not really see how horribly accusing its aspect had become, because she could not rid her mind's eye, first of the crisis of the 9th, and secondly of certain silken cobwebs that hung about her head. For in her feverish restlessness that night all her thoughts, even those of bitterest remorse, came to her—like light passing through gauze—through a confused vision of the autumn styles and modes.

Next morning when she brought Bringas his chocolate, she found him cheerful and energetic, singing songs to himself. She, on the other hand, was unusually subdued. Later Cándida came in with some small articles that Rosalía had bought at *Sobrino's*; she was generally entrusted with the task of bringing such things to the Palace, so that Don Francisco would not grow suspicious. But Rosalía was so preoccupied with thoughts of disaster that morning that she hardly looked at the organdie and embroidery silks and hurriedly bundled them away in a chest of drawers. She expected Pez's reply at eleven. Bringas invariably left for the office at about 10.30, but that day he was less punctual than usual. While he was eating breakfast all the cheerfulness with which he had waked disappeared, because Paquito began to read him some of the clandestine papers which were going the rounds of Madrid, making threats against the Queen and declaring that the fall of the Monarchy was imminent. Don Francisco was furious.

"If you bring any of those filthy things here again," he said, "I'll take you away from the University and put you in a shop in the Calle de Toledo."

And he left the house fuming.

Soon after he had gone, Rosalía received the letter she was expecting. 'It's not very thick,' she thought, her soul hanging by a thread, and she went off to the *Camón* to open it in private, for Cándida was roaming about the house and she had eyes like arrows. 'It isn't very thick,' she said to herself again, as she opened the envelope and took out a piece of paper—'There's nothing else.' And in effect there was nothing in the envelope but a letter, written in Pez's clear, neat hand. Rosalía felt such anger when she saw that there were no banknotes enclosed with the letter that at first she could not read it. The piece of paper trembled in her hand, and she only read a line here and there, looking for the key to its meaning. In a few seconds she had mastered it. And each sentence she read clawed at her vitals as if the words were talons.

"He was very much grieved, desolate, not to be able to oblige her at the moment; but it was quite impossible. He had found his household lamentably behind in every way, with an enormous accumulation of unpaid bills. His situation was not at all what it appeared to be.

245

He could say without exaggeration, and under the seal of confidence, that all the ostentation which was seen in his household was only an attempt to keep up appearances. In spite of this he would have rushed to his friend's assistance, if a bill had not come due that very day which it was impossible to avoid paying. However, later on . . ."

Rosalía could not read any more, she was blind with anger and shame. She tore the letter into small pieces— if she could only have done the same to the vile creature who had written it. For he was vile; she had told him that it was a question of her honour and of the peace of her household. What creatures men were! She had thought that some of them at least were gentlemen; but what a mistake she had made. And it was for this that she had debased herself—as she had debased herself. She deserved to have her husband drive her away from that honourable hearth. It was ignominy enough to sell yourself, but to give yourself away! At this point tears of grief and anger ran down her cheeks; they were the first that she had shed since her marriage, for the tears she had wept when her children had been seriously ill were tears of quite another kind.

But the worst thing about it was that she was done for after all. If she was not at the Inquisitor's house that afternoon at three o'clock with the money in her hand . . . He would wait until three o'clock . . . until three o'clock, but not a moment more. And to whom, *Virgin del Carmen*, to whom could she turn? Although she recommended herself fervently to all the Saints and all the Virgins, her spirit could no longer find any peace in this. There seemed to be no room left in her mind for anything but desperation. But just when she was abandoning herself hopelessly to despair, a sudden ray of hope shone through her darkly clouded mind—*Refugio!*

246

Yes. Torres had told her only a few days before that Refugio had been to Trujillo's house to receive ten thousand reals which her sister had sent her for the expenses of starting her business.

XLII

Time was pressing; it was not possible to stop and consider the propriety of the step she was taking: it was midday already. 'Rather than have Bringas find me out,' she thought, hurriedly putting on her mantilla. 'I would suffer anything, I would even debase myself by asking this favour of a . . .' She left the sentence unfinished.

Refugio lived in the Calle de Bordadores, opposite the small Plaza de San Gines. When she got there, Rosalía was surprised to see how respectable-looking the house was, and still more surprised, when she went in, at the cleanness of the staircase. She had expected a disgusting entrance in a disorderly neighbourhood, but the neighbourhood and the tenants of the house could hardly have been quieter. In the basement there was a shop which sold bronze ornaments for ecclesiastical purposes, and on the ground floor a large warehouse of Bejar velveteens, while the first floor contained the office of a religious paper. Rosalía's spirits rose a little, and they needed this encouragement, for she felt as if she were going to the gallows.

'What necessity can do!' she thought bitterly, as she reached the second floor and put her hand to the bell rope. 'Who could ever have made me believe that I would drink this water? Now the only thing lacking is for her to be rude to me and my shame and punishment will be complete.'

Refugio herself opened the door and was surprised to see who was there. Rosalía, in her nervousness, vacillated between smiles and gravity, not knowing whether to be familiar with Refugio, or courteously distant to her.

It was a nice question, and provided a problem in social relations for which it would have been difficult to find a solution. On the way from the door to the sitting room, they only exchanged a few words, half-phrases and monosyllables.

"Come in here," Refugio said, showing Rosalía into what seemed to be a sort of dressing room. "Celestina, help me clear some of these things off."

Celestina must be the servant—or so Rosalia thought in those first moments; but later on had reason to correct this opinion. Her appearance was as strange as Refugio's, and indeed remarkably similar, so that it would not have been easy to say which of the two was the lady of the house. "Probably neither of them is," thought the Señora de Bringas acutely, as she seated herself in the chair which had been cleared for her.

The Sánchez girl's handsome hair was in the greatest disorder, and had obviously not been combed that day, and her bust was only covered by a thin lawn corset-cover, so carelessly fastened that it showed half of an abundant bosom. Her feet were thrust into canvas slippers in such a slipshod way that the heels were clacking loosely on the tile floor.

"I would put on a dress," Refugio said, pushing aside a pile of clothing which was on the sofa so that she could sit down, "but as I'm among friends."

"Yes, of course, my dear, don't bother," said the Señora de Bringas, confirmed in her idea of the necessity of being amiable. "With this heat—"

As she said it she could not help looking round her; never in her life had she seen anything like the disorder in the apartment, nor such a wild, slovenly confusion of good things with bad. The sitting-room, which could be seen through the half-open doors, looked like the back room of a shop; on top of all the chairs were trimmed hats and untrimmed hats, pieces of ribbon, odd bits of cloth and ravellings. Cardboard boxes which had lost their covers displayed bunches of expensive artificial flowers, all tumbled about and damaged as if they were worthless. Some of them looked so faded and withered that they almost seemed to be asking to be watered. Besides these things, there were *fichus*, trimmed with jet or silk cording, linen chemises and pieces of embroidery. And this chaotic mass of objects extended to the dressing-room, and invaded chairs and sofa, and mixed itself up with the clothes that were in use, as if a revolutionary hand had tried to prevent even the possibility of order. Two or three of Refugio's own dresses, turned inside out and showing their linings with their sleeves dilated, yawned upon the chairs, and one bronze kid boot was standing under the table, while its mate had climbed upon it.

The furniture was a strange mixture too; the night table was of the cheapest kind—iron varnished black with painted flowers. But on the mantelpiece a very elegant bronze clock was indignantly associating with two gilded china dogs in the worst possible taste and with broken ears. All the pictures were crooked, and one of the curtains had been pulled off its rod; while the floor was covered with stains and the chimney of the hanging lamp was black with smoke. Through the half-closed door into the bedroom Rosalía had a view of a large gilded brass bedstead, unmade, and with the bedclothes in great disorder, as if someone had just risen from it.

Refugio imagined that the Señora de Bringas had come to see the articles she had for sale, yielding at last to her solicitations.

"You have come rather late," she said. "I have sold almost everything. But I am no good at it. I don't know what my sister was thinking of when she decided to set

me up as a shopkeeper. Since I've been at it I've done nothing but lose money; half the people who buy things don't pay me, and I can't bring myself to dun them. Really the sooner I get rid of everything the better. A lot of ladies are still coming to see my things, and they are carrying off the little I have left."

"Just the same," Rosalía said, picking up some *marabouts* and aigrettes, "there are some charming things here."

"Do you like those aigrettes?" Refugio asked, delighted to show herself generous to Rosalía. "Do take them— I mean as a present."

"Oh no, I couldn't think of it . . ."

"Yes, yes, do. I should be delighted. Anyway, it would be better than my selling them and never being paid! And here's a hat," she added, going into the sitting room, and returning with one. "Let me give it to you. It isn't trimmed, but you could choose some ribbons you liked for it."

Rosalía was amazed at this generosity, and was inclined to look more benevolently at Refugio, though she continued to refuse the presents.

"Are you slighting me because I am poor?" the girl asked reproachfully.

If Rosalía's need for money had not been so acute that it forced her to endure everything, she would certainly have rejected these attentions with which this woman— so much her inferior from every point of view—was trying to raise herself to Rosalía's level. But she could not afford to be haughty at the very moment when she was going to ask a favour, and a favour that debased her so much! Several times she tried to pronounce the words, · and could not force herself to do it. She almost decided not to say anything, and to escape from the house. But the inflexible law of necessity fixed her there: she was obliged to drink this cup. 'Now that I have made the sacrifice of coming here' she thought, 'I must not leave without at least trying to get the money.'

Time was pressing more than ever: one o'clock had struck already. Two or three times she managed to bring the words to her lips, but could not get them out. In the end she had to struggle so hard to pronounce them that the words came out haltingly, while the poor woman fanned herself busily, pretending that what she was saying was of no great importance, and making heroic efforts to appear calm and not to blush.

"Well, now . . . Refugio, I want to talk about something else. I have come to ask a favour of you."

"A favour of me?" the girl asked, with the liveliest curiosity.

"Yes, a favour," Rosalía went on, rather disconcerted by the curiosity. "That is, if you can manage it. If you can't, we needn't say any more about it."

"But tell me what it is."

"Well, if you can . . ." the lady said, swallowing the bitterness that was almost choking her. "The fact is that I need a sum of money; and I have been told that you have some, that you cashed a considerable amount at Trujillo's. Well, then, if you could let me have five thousand reals for a few days, I would be extremely grateful—I mean of course, if you can spare it."

XLIII

And how relieved she felt when she had got it out! It seemed as if a great weight in her breast grew lighter. Refugio heard her calmly enough, not even seeming unduly surprised. Then she made a curious moue with her mouth, and said:

"I'll tell you how it is. I have got the money, but I don't know if I could use it like that. Tomorrow I have to pay some big bills."

She scrutinized her visitor impertinently; and after a pause in which she seemed to be studying a sum in arithmetic placed just between Rosalía's eyebrows, continued:

"You understand ... it isn't that I lack money ..."

Here she picked up what seemed to be her sewing box, and drew out from the bottom of it a handful of things— bits of cloth, unwound threads and banknotes, all mixed up together.

"You see, I have the money, but ..."

Rosalía's spirits lightened when she saw the notes; but the shadows darkened again, when the wicked Sanchez girl put the money back in the box and shook her head.

"No, I can't, señora, I really can't ..."

'This wretch wants me to humiliate myself even more than I have done already, to beg and supplicate and throw myself at her feet so that she can trample on me. Swine! If I could only have you whipped! What greater honour could you ask for than to lend money to someone like me?'

But naturally she did not say what she was thinking; she had instead to call up the honeyed expression which seemed suited to the nature of the occasion.

"Think it over, my dear, you may find that you can do it after all. You might be able to put off your creditors for a few days, while I . . ."

"There is nothing I would like better," the other answered, with affected commiseration. "I feel it very much that you should have to go away empty-handed."

The protecting nature of the phrase exasperated Rosalía. She could have caught the girl by her abundant hair and dragged that snout along the ground.

"Can't you make an effort?" she asked, drawing strength from the inmost depths of her breast.

"I only wish I could! I am so sorry not to be able to help you. Believe me, I really feel it. I would do anything to help you and Don Francisco."

"No," said Rosalía quickly, wounded by this introduction of her husband's name. "This is entirely my own affair. Please leave my husband out of it. It is my affair, entirely my affair . . ."

"Ah! . . ." murmured Refugio, staring fixedly at the spot between Rosalía's eyebrows once more.

The señora noticed that after gazing at her for a few moments, the cursed wretch began to fumble in her sewing box again . . . Was she going to soften at last and take out the notes? No. She made a gesture, as if of a person who is forcing herself to harden her heart and overcome her weakness, and said again:

"I can't do it, I really can't. And if I won't do it for you, no one else could make me. For you or for Don Francisco I would do anything, I'd give you my last piece of bread. Believe me, sometimes I am afraid of the weakness of my own character. I am so silly that I believe if you wept, I would be foolish enough to lend you the money. And it would be foolish, because I need it very much myself."

"Never!" thought Rosalía, turned into a basilisk. "This shameless creature wants me to kneel in front of her—it's a sight she'll never see."

But out loud she only said with an affected calmness which she was far from feeling.

"If it would need such means of extortion, there is nothing more to be said."

"I can't do it, I really can't. I have such enormous debts to pay," the Sánchez girl said, in the tone of one who puts an end to a subject.

"Very well then, we'll say no more about it."

"And you didn't go to the baths after all?"

This complete change of subject disconcerted Rosalía. The leaf seemed to have been turned over, and with it all hope of a loan. She answered the foolish question with the first words that came into her head, and as she did so, such a wave of heat flooded over her that she could have thrown herself into water to prevent her body from burning itself away.

"My dear," she said, "it's dreadfully hot in here."

"Wait a minute," Refugio said, "I'll close the shutters to keep out the light."

Rosalía, her soul hanging on a thread, gazed at the prints of bullfighters which adorned the walls. But she saw them confused with the agonized uneasiness of her mind. In the end her anxiety conquered her dignity, and she did not hesitate to humiliate herself a little more. She gave Refugio a little tap on the knee with her fan, and said, managing, not without a great effort, a lightly affectionate tone.

"Come, my dear lend me the money."

"What?" asked Refugio, in apparent surprise. "Oh, the money. Do you know I had forgotten all about it. Frankly, I'd always thought that you lent money on interest, not that you had to borrow it."

Rosalía would gladly have replied to this malicious observation by pulling out those uncombed locks; but she had to submit to everything.

"I need the money very much," she said, "I *must* pay a debt. If you like I can give you interest—whatever suits you."

"Jesus! Don't insult me. If I lent you the money—and I do so regret not being in a position to do so—I wouldn't think of charging interest. After all it's between members of *the family*."

When the daughter of the Pipaóns heard that remotely connected baggage describe herself as *one of the family*, she nearly lost her self-control. The torture was almost too great to be endured without some outburst. But she gritted her teeth and managed to make a face which resembled a smile. 'I must be foaming at the mouth,' she thought. 'If I don't go soon, I shall have an attack of something.'

Refugio put her hand in the sewing box, and drew out the bills again. Jesus! If at last she should decide to do it! Rosalía watched her movements with dissimulated anxiety as the girl handled the bills one by one as if she were counting them, and finally declared—"Ah, señora, it's impossible, impossible."

Still she did not stuff the roll of bills back where it had been, but put it on the mantelpiece; and this detail revived Rosalía's dying hopes.

"You see," the girl said, throwing herself down in the armchair in an abandoned way as if it were a bed, so that her feet almost touched the lady's knees. "All this business here has ruined me. I went into it without understanding it at all. And as I haven't a strong will, everyone has taken advantage of me. In the beginning everything was wonderful! My things went like hot cakes; the ladies simply came and carried them off—of course they were the best quality and not dear. But when the question of

payment came up, I wish you could have heard them.
'You must wait until next week'—'Come around for it
later—' 'I haven't got it now—' 'Come back again.' And
in the end I had nothing but poverty and unpaid debts.

"Ah, what a place Madrid is, all show! A gentleman
I know says that it's as if the Carnival went on all the year
round, with the poor dressing up as rich people. For here,
except for half a dozen families, everyone is poor. Façade,
nothing but façade. These people have no idea of comfort
in their houses. They live in the streets; and so that they
can dress well and go to the theatre, some families eat
nothing but potato omelettes all the year round. I know
wives of small officials who are unemployed half the
year, and they dress so that it's a pleasure to meet them.
They look like duchesses, and their children look like
princes and princesses. How do they do it? I simply can't
imagine. A gentleman friend of mine says that Madrid
is full of these mysteries. Some people, as I say, don't
eat, so that they can dress instead; but others manage
it in other ways—Oh, I have heard stories, I've seen a
lot of the world. Women like that are out for what they
can get—they buy their clothes in any way they can. And
then they talk about other women—as if they weren't
worse themselves!

"Well, the result of all this is that I've only been paid
for half the things I've sold. The rest are walking about
the streets, and nobody in the world could get a penny for
them. Cheating liars! And then they come here giving
themselves such airs. 'You great—' I say to myself—
inside me of course—'I don't deceive anyone: I live
honestly by my work. But you are all lies and pretences,
and want to make yourself silk dresses out of poor
people's bread.' And you ought to hear them criticizing
other women, and despising them. There was even one
who looked down her nose at me, and did her best to

259

get out of paying anything; and then came here begging me for money. And what did she want it for? Very likely to give to her lover."

As she spoke, with a heat and emphasis that showed how much she felt her subject, she turned a burning glare on the unfortunate postulant. And Rosalía sat silent, with excessively distended nostrils and downcast eyes; and though she breathed with difficulty, reined herself in and controlled her furious desire to do or say something violent.

XLIV

"For this insolence," Rosalía said to herself, "for this cynicism with which you speak about ladies whose shoes you aren't worth to take off, you deserve to have that viper's tongue torn out by the roots and to be whipped through the streets naked down to the waist— Like this! This! This!" In her mind she struck the blows on the living flesh. She was in such a state, and had to exert such force to contain herself, that she began to feel she would prefer any domestic catastrophe whatever to the horrible torment she was undergoing.

"I must leave this place," she thought, "I can't stand any more. I'd rather have my husband despise me and enslave me than have this wretch spitting in my face as she is doing now."

But as she thought this, the figure of Torquemada rose before her, explaining to Don Francisco the obligation of the husband to pay his wife's debts; and she imagined that husband's fury. No, with all her power of imagination she could not conjure up a picture of Bringas as he would be at that moment: he had such a horror of lies and deceptions.

'Rather than have him find out,' she thought, 'I'll endure anything. I'll even let this slut walk over me. After all, it's only I who suffer this shame. No one else knows about it, no one can throw it in my face.'

"A gentleman friend of mine," Refugio remarked, passing from a tone of angry conviction to one of jovial lightness, "says that there's nothing but poverty in Madrid, that there's no true aristocracy, and that the greater part of those who pass for rich and distinguished are only common people. And really, in what other country in the world would you see a titled lady like the Tellería go around begging someone to lend her a thousand reals, as she came begging me. There have been people in Madrid who have shot themselves because they lost seven hundred reals at cards, and when some young sprig spends a hundred duros on a woman, they say he has ruined his family. And I don't even mention those who apparently live on air, who go to the theatre on passes, ride on the railways with free tickets and even wear handed-down clothes. All for show! When I meet people like that I begin to feel proud, because anyway I don't owe anything, and if I did I would pay it. I live by my work and no one has the right to question what I do. I don't deceive anyone, and if people don't like me, they can leave me alone. You understand what I mean? Because . . . Celestina, go to the Levante and tell them to bring us some coffee. You'll have coffee with us, won't you?"

"No, thank you," Rosalía said dully; her forces were exhausted.

She got up to go. The woman was so repugnant to her and wounded her pride so intensely with the coarseness of her expressions and the vulgarity of her ideas, that she would not humiliate herself any more. But Refugio detained her by catching her arm, and saying with a loud laugh:

"Won't you really have some coffee with us? Wait a little while, I was just beginning to think of giving you the money after all."

Rosalía sat down, her spirits rising with the words. The devil standing in front of her making indecent faces suddenly became human and even agreeable.

"It's a quarter past two," she breathed, obliged to smile, and beginning to find a charm in the uneven teeth of the girl.

"At what hour do you have to pay?"

"At three o'clock," the other answered quickly.

"Oh then, there's plenty of time," Refugio said.

A door slammed as Celestina went out to order the coffee. The girl stretched herself in the chair again, in an attitude which was not so much lazy as indecent, and said, between bursts of rude laughter:

"If La Señora were here, you wouldn't be in these straits, because you could always throw yourself at her feet and burst into tears ... They say La Señora helps all her friends who go to her with stories about their troubles. Well I must say that if I had all the money of the country in my hands as she has, I'd do it too. And now a gentleman friend of mine tells me that something really is going to happen soon."

'But how many gentlemen friends have you got?—you prostitute,' Rosalía would have said if she had been a position to do so. 'You seem to be on terms with all the male members of the human race!'

"Yes. We are going to have a change of air," Refugio went on insolently. "We are going to get rid of the whole lot. Liberty is coming, liberties ..."

This lack of respect in speaking of Her Majesty so infuriated Rosalía that she was on the point of throwing all circumspection to the winds and attacking the infamous wretch, saying to her: 'How dare you speak like that, you ...' A few well chosen monosyllables would have been enough. With one of her wide careless gestures, the Sánchez girl had knocked a little basket off the mantelpiece, and a box of cigarettes fell out of it. 'So you smoke too, do you, you pig?' Rosalía would have added to her denunciation if she could have spoken spontaneously; but she had to watch the girl pick up the box from the floor and say nothing.

Before long the boy brought the coffee and left the tray on the dressing table, though it was not easy to find room for it there; and Refugio and Celestina, after repeating their invitation to Rosalía who still refused to take anything, served themselves. The two girls seemed to be on precisely the same footing and called each other *thou* with every appearance of equality. It was impossible to say which was servant and which was mistress, although Celestina was perhaps a trifle more disorderly looking than Refugio.

"Virgin del Carmen!" Rosalía exclaimed within herself. "What have I got mixed up with! If the Lord brings me safely out of this, I'll never get myself into such a position again."

"Celestina," Refugio asked in a friendly tone, "aren't I going to have my hair done today?"

The other girl excused her delay by saying how much she had to do. Nothing had been cleared up yet, the dressing room was like a lion's cage and the bedroom was no better. When the girls finished their coffee and Celestina began to try to produce some order in the dressing room, Rosalía could not control her impatience any longer and closed her fan with a loud clack.

"It must be very late. Quarter to three, I should think," she said.

"The trouble is—" Refugio said, playing with her victim, "the trouble is that—I've just now remembered—I can't, I really can't give you anything at all. I'd forgotten that it's today that I've got to pay a debt of two thousand odd reals."

Rosalía felt as if a snake had wound itself around her chest and was crushing her. She could not speak. She would gladly have launched herself at the wretch and left the mark of her ten nails on her devil's face. But we can seldom do what we wish. She rose—she could only make a guttural sound, a weak expression of her rage, controlled as it was by dignity.

'She is playing with me like a cat with a mouse,' she thought. 'I must go, if I stay here I will have a fit.'

"Wait a minute," Refugio said. "I've thought of something. I've promised to help you, and I won't go back on it. The word of a Sánchez Emperador is an Emperor's word after all, and especially when its a matter of *the family*."

'Leave the family out of your disgusting mouth.' Rosalía longed to say.

The girl went on:

"It's occurred to me that I could get the money from a woman friend of mine."

"But do you realise how late it is?" Rosalía asked, regaining her lost hopes.

"Oh, she lives quite close, in the Calle de la Sal."

"But you haven't even begun to get ready."

"Oh, I've time enough to have my hair done still. Celestina!"

"There's no time," Rosalía said.

Refugio went into her bedroom, and called from there "My corset!" And Rosalía hurried to her with it and helped her hook it up. And while this operation was going on, the impertinent wretch was impudent enough to say:

"The Señor de Pez might well have saved you from these difficulties. But you don't always catch him with money. The poor thing hasn't got a penny just now."

The wife of Bringas said nothing. Shame burned her face and constricted her heart. What she did do was pull the corset together and draw furiously on the laces as if she wanted to cut the body of the she-devil in two.

"Señora, for God's sake, you are cutting me in half. I don't lace myself in like that; I leave such tight lacing to plump people who want to look like sylphs. What do you think, shall I have my hair dressed?"

"No. Catch up your hair with a ribbon—I like it very much like that—I like it better. You look like the Herodias in one of the pictures in the Palace. Do hurry, fix your hair. See how late it is. Here, I'll help you."

Refugio seated herself, and the Señora de Bringas arranged the abundant locks in a figure-eight.

"What a lady's maid I've got," Refugio said, laughing. "Such an honour!"

And when she was finally ready to go out, she began to sing and whirl herself around the dressing room, and then, to Rosalía's alarm, sat down calmly in an armchair.

"But really—" the lady exclaimed furiously.

In her mind there was a commotion like that which occurs in large clocks when they are just going to strike the hour.

The girl remarked with deliberate calmness:

"It's so hot. I don't feel like going out."

"But you—are you playing with me, or what?"

"Don't be alarmed, Señora, and don't get on your high horse," the Sánchez girl said. "If you try any of your haughty ways on me, it's all over. You can stay in your house and I'll stay in mine. Here are the five thousand reals. Look at them, there they are. I'm going to give them to you, so that I won't have to go out now. And I'll get what I need later on."

XLV

But still she did not hand the money over, and Rosalía was on hot coals.

"I'm going to give you some good advice," the wretched girl went on, "to show you what an interest I take in the family. It's this. Don't get too intimate with Doña Milagros; she could turn the most sensible person's head. Stay in your own corner, in the shade of your good man, and leave off these romances . . . And don't go to Sobrino's shop any more: it's out of your class. And don't trust the Tellería when she makes up to you, she's very sly and a terrible flatterer."

Rosalía could only sit, nodding her head in agreement. Finally the girl put the bills in her hand. And what peace descended on the unfortunate lady's soul when she had the money in her possession at last! She got up to go at once, afraid that this she-devil might try to take the money back again.

"What, are you going?"

"It's very late, I haven't a moment to lose. You know how grateful I am to you. Oh—shall we draw up an agreement?"

"There's no need," Refugio said haughtily, taking up a noble and disinterested attitude. "As it's between members of the family. This afternoon I'll send you the hat and the other little things."

"Thank you."

"Wait a moment until I tell you something."

"What is it?" Rosalía asked, alarmed again.

"I'm going to tell you what the Marquesa de Tellería said about you."

"Said about me?"

"Yes, about you ... Right here, sitting in this very chair. I can still see her. It was the day before she went away to the baths. She came to buy some artificial flowers from me. She was talking about you and she said—I can't help laughing—she said you were dowdy!"

Rosalía was petrified. The phrase wounded her to the quick: she had never before received such a blow. And as she was hurrying away down the staircase, the pain of this wound to her self-esteem tormented her more than those she had received in her honour. *Dowdy*—the frightful anathema engraved itself on her mind and seemed to be stamped there for eternity like a brand in the living flesh.

'God alone knows what I have suffered today,' she thought, as the carriage took her to Torquemada's house. 'What a Golgotha!'

When she arrived she hurried upstairs, for it had already struck three. But luckily she found the Inquisitor still there, though he was already getting impatient and was ready to set off to the Palace. He received her with smiles and asked after the health of her family. That day the adoration of the doughnut formed by his fingers did not annoy her as much as usual. The happiness of escaping from so great a danger, and of getting rid of such an antipathetic creditor left her no attention to spare for irritating details. Shortening the session as much as she could, she took her leave. The humiliations of the day had left her terribly nervous.

'Milagros *can't* have said that about me,' she thought, as she was on her way back to the Palace, still tormented by the horrible inscription that seemed to be burning on her forehead. 'It's simply a lie of that wretch's. What a day it has been! The first thing I shall do when I get home is look to see if I've got any gray hairs. I well might have.'

And in fact the first thing she did was look in the mirror. But let us say at once to tranquilize those ladies who find themselves in a similar case, that no white hairs had appeared. And if they had, she would soon have found a way of concealing them.

However it is an indubitable fact that the disappointments and humiliations of those days left the lady so worn out and in such low spirits that her husband began to think she must be ill.

"Something is wrong with you. Don't deny it. Would you like to have the doctor in? Now you see—if you'd only bathed at the *Jeronimos* as I urged you to, you'd be another person now."

But she assured him that nothing was the matter with her; and when the doctor came he could not find any definite ailment. It was all a matter of those wretched nerves, it seemed. The most striking symptoms were her sadness and a tendency to be needlessly alarmed for the slightest causes, combined with a lack of appetite. There was also noticeable a new manner of behaving towards her husband. Although her estimation for him had declined considerably, the outwards forms of respect she showed exhibited a good deal of care and refinement. This may have had a number of recondite causes, but in the impossibility of getting to the bottom of these, we will have to recur to hypothesis and see in her behaviour something resembling the wheedlings practised on Customs officers by people who want to pass contraband goods. Rosalía was often in fact merely making use of this pacific and venal means of placating her husband while she was bringing to light her hidden store of handsome clothes. For one by one things were appearing. Almost every day Don Francisco would notice something new, and a discussion would follow in which Rosalía would try to gain her ends with amusing fictions and caresses and endearments.

But she did not always succeed in this, and the good man began to be seriously preoccupied about the provenance of these luxurious articles of dress, which kept appearing from nowhere like theatrical surprises. More than once he was inflexible in his demand for explanations, and produced such an arsenal of unanswerable questions that his wife trembled like a criminal before the weight of evidence. But she was gradually learning to harden herself against these unwarranted examinations, beginning by not taking them too much to heart or caring whether her husband believed her stories or not. She had finally decided to explain her irregularities only with the incontrovertible logic of *because it is*, when a very grave event put an end to her difficulties, for the Customs officer went almost out of his mind and forgot his duties completely.

The cause of this mental and moral overthrow occurred in the following way. One morning Don Francisco went to the office as tranquilly as usual; but he had hardly put his elbows on the table when one of his fellow workers, Señor de Vargas, came up to him and whispered "The Navy has revolted." This sounded so absurd to Bringas that he began to laugh; but Vargas insisted, gave details and repeated the text of telegrams. Don Francisco was for a time completely dazed by this news, like someone who has had a blow on the head. And as if this was not enough, the other went on to even more lugubrious statements: "It's the Deluge, friend Bringas, now it really is upon us."

The poor man finally pulled himself together a little and went with Vargas and some of the other employees to the office of the assistant Director (the Director of course was in San Sebastian); and there they found various other members of the Royal Household, all in a state of the greatest consternation.

"But it's very serious . . . How can it have happened? Well, you see, as soon as they had the ships . . . But what is the Government doing? They must send troops immediately . . . It's an avalanche . . . Cadiz has risen, Seville has risen, all Andalusia has caught fire . . . Poor Señora, everyone told her what would happen, but she wouldn't pay any attention . . . And the generals who were sent to the Canaries? They are in Cadiz. And Prim? On his way to Barcelona . . . In short everything is breaking down."

This was on the 19th. Bringas returned home more dead than alive. All that day and the days that followed he seemed to be almost crazy. He could not eat or sleep, and spent his time in asking everyone for news—embracing almost with tears those whose news was encouraging and driving away harshly those who brought bad tidings. The poor man became completely indifferent to everything, even to household affairs. If his wife had dressed herself up as the Empress of Golconda during those first few days he wouldn't even have noticed it. With the loss of his appetite his health seemed to break up completely. He had difficulty in walking and found it hard to pronounce certain words, and his eyes began to trouble him again. It was such a pity. They had seemed so completely recovered that he had even been thinking of finishing the hair picture—there was only a very little left to do.

"Ah well," he would say to himself, "if this infamous thing succeeds, I shall die."

Rosalía and Paquito were very depressed too, although it must be confessed that the former had moments in which she felt more curiosity than grief. The revolution was a bad thing of course, everyone said so. But it was also the unknown—and the unknown attracts exalted imaginations, and particularly seduces people who have got themselves into some irregular situation. With other times there will be other ways of existence, something new, stupendous which will give their natures play.

'After all,' she thought, 'we must wait and see what happens.'

Pez continued to visit them; but she had taken such an aversion to him that she hardly addressed him. The proud lady's thoughts on that subject were so many and so varied that it would be impossible to reproduce them. But one was a determination never again to fish for creatures of so little substance. She imagined herself casting her bait in deep and well defined seas, through whose waters swam gallant sharks, pompous whales and fishes of real weight. Her day-dreaming mind carried her forward to the coming winter, when she intended to launch a social campaign which would be both enter-taining and profitable. She would eschew the society of the Pezs and Tellerías and all such persons of uncertain financial position, and seek more solid and efficacious support among the Fucars, the Trujillos, the Cimarras and other families of the indubitable aristocracy.

XLVI

It was the end of the world! Don Francisco heard—
groaning as he listened—that Bejar had declared for the
revolutionaries too, and Santona and Santander and other
cities as well. Señor de Pez, with unexampled cruelty,
told his friend that he did not think that such a landslide
could be stopped. It was obvious that the Queen had lost
her throne and that there was nothing left for her to do
take refuge in France. How often he had prophesied it,
how often he had prognosticated what was happening
now!

Cándida, however, brought good tidings:

"Novaliches has left with an immense army, but really
immense . . . You'll see how he'll disperse them before
you can say Jesus! . . . They are saying that some of the
Andalusian towns have beaten off the rebels. There are
a lot of people here who like to frighten you, so they
paint everything larger than life. I've heard that things
aren't nearly as bad as they say."

Bringas embraced her:

"And Prim, where is Prim?" he asked.

"I've heard he has been shot—or that he's going to
be shot. I'm sure that if the Queen would only take
courage and come back to Madrid and show herself to
the crowds and address them, saying: *"You are all my
children"*, everything would collapse.

Bringas was of the same opinion. But he would have
liked even better to have Narvaez come back to life,
which was difficult to arrange.

"Oh, if Don Ramon were only alive!" he kept saying.
"Because if they don't settle this quickly, we are going

273

to have bloodshed in Madrid. There are so few soldiers that these democrats or demagogues (or whatever they call themselves) will seize the town and we will have a guillotine in every square."

Every day the poor man failed a little more in health, and he was amazed at the tranquillity of his fellow-workers. For they had all taken the catastrophe extremely calmly, and did not seem to think it impossible that they might find place in some other office—any kind of office whatever—if the revolution made a clean sweep of the Privy Purse. But the very thought of this defection was so shocking to Bringas that he declared that he would rather beg for alms in the streets than ask the revolutionaries for a position.

"But, my dear, don't worry yourself about that," his wife said. "You can always go back to work in the *Holy Places*."

"But do you really think, silly creature, that there will be any Holy Places then? You'll see what will happen: guillotines, bloodshed, atheism, shamelessness. And in the end the Nations will send their armies—they may be on the way already—to the aid of our Queen. I say that the Nations will come and divide up our poor country among them."

When the news of the battle of Alcolea reached Madrid, the poor man almost had an apoplectic fit. And that was the day that Madrid declared itself for the revolutionaries too. Paquito brought the bad news. He had been passing through the Puerto del Sol and had found it packed with people. A general was haranguing the crowd, while another was tearing off his epaulettes. And afterwards the people dispersed and went running down the streets, showing every sign of rejoicing rather than of panic. Groups were marching up and down shouting *Long Live the Revolution—the Navy—the Army*, and saying that Isabella *II*

274

was no longer Queen. Men went by carrying banners with various revolutionary inscriptions on them, while others were busy taking down the Royal Crowns from shop fronts.

Paquito described it all vividly to his father, only trying to minimize the parts that he thought would be particularly painful to him. The poor boy had to hide his real feelings, because, though his ideas had been moulded on his father's opinions, he was only a boy after all, and he could not help being seduced by the fascination which the idea of Liberty has on all young opening minds, when they are just beginning to play with the notions they have gleaned from their historical and social studies. As he was describing the scenes of the day in a tone of grief and consternation, a strange, incomprehensible feeling of pleasure spread through his whole body. He could not understand it at all. But it undoubtedly came from the fact that his soul had not been sufficiently on guard against the expansive exhilaration in the city, and had breathed it in as lungs breathe the same air which those around them are inhaling.

"There is nothing more to be done," Bringas said, drawing strength from the very intensity of his despair. "It is time to prepare ourselves. God's will be done. Resignation. The crowds will soon invade the Palace to loot it, and they will spare no one. Let us show ourselves worthy, accept our martyrdom . . ."

He choked on something in his throat. They were all silent, listening to the sounds that came in from the passages and from the great court yard below. There was great alarm in the Palace-city. All the inhabitants kept coming to their doors to get news or to communicate their own impressions. And some of them even went downstairs, anxious to learn if anything was happening outside. But silence reigned in the court yard, and though

275

the doors were open, not a living creature entered. Then when they were least expecting it, Doña Cándida suddenly appeared in a terrible state, saying between stifled groans:

"It's coming . . . it's coming . . ."

"What is coming, Señora, for heaven's sake, what is it?"

"The sack of the Palace . . . Oh, my dear Don Francisco, I've seen the crowds coming down the Calle de Lepanto. Oh, what horrible people, what criminal faces, what rough beards and filthy hands! We will all have our throats cut."

"But what has become of the Palace Guard . . . the halberdiers?"

"They must have risen too. They are all the same. God help us!"

There was a moment of panic, but it was of short duration, for when the Bringas went out into the passage they found some of their neighbours walking up and down as calmly as if nothing were going on.

"But what is happening?"

"Nothing. A few boys made a disturbance in the doorway, and the Town Council have sent a guard."

Paquito insisted on going downstairs much against his father's wishes, for the good man was afraid of something happening to him. But the boy returned safely before long.

"There's a guard of peasants below," he said.

"Have they got arms?"

"Yes, they have those they were given in the park this afternoon. But they are very quiet well-behaved people. Some of them are wearing hats and others caps and some have berets—it looks as if they were doing it for a joke."

"This is a fine time for jokes! Where are the soldiers?"

"They have retired to their barracks."

"Holy Father!" That means that we are in the power of the *canaille*, the *sans-culottes*, the *so-called* masses . . ."

"They have put up a notice board which reads: *Palace of the Nation, guarded by the People.*"

"And fine care they will take of it, no doubt!" Bringas said, with intense grief. "There won't be a thread left in the Palace. The only good thing is that they'll have so much to destroy below that by the time they get up here . . ."

The anxiety in the Palace continued all night, and Bringas along with many of the other inhabitants did not go to bed at all and got in supplies of food to last them for a number of days. They were afraid of being attacked by the mob at any moment. But to their great surprise not the least sound disturbed the august peace of the Palace. It seemed as if the Monarchical Institution were still sleeping in it as quietly and peacefully as in better days.

On the morning of the 30th Cándida appeared, quite out of breath.

"Do you know what has happened?" she asked, without even saying good morning.

"What is it, Señora, what has happened?" They all asked at the same time, in the greatest anxiety, thinking that something stupendous must have occured.

"Why only that those poor people who are guarding the Palace have had nothing to eat since they came here yesterday afternoon. No one has remembered to send them anything. I don't know what the Committee is thinking about—because there's a Committee that they call revolutionary—or the Town Council either. It's really pathetic to see them. I went down this morning to talk to them, and really, Don Francisco, they are the most harmless creatures, innocents. If they don't send us any *sans-culottes* except these we can sleep in peace. Some of them have gone up to the Royal Apartments and are walking about lost in wonder, staring at the ceilings, and others are asking the way to the kitchens. It's painful to

277

see them so hungry—I can't tell you how sorry I felt for them. Some of my neighbours on the Third Floor have sent them down what they could spare, but it was nothing among so many—there are twenty mouths for each omelette and fifty for each bottle of wine."

"In short there's nothing to be afraid of, they are perfect lambs. Rob? They haven't pulled a blade of grass. Kill? Nothing but a few doves. Two or three of the men have been amusing themselves trying to shoot them, but they haven't had much luck—revolutionaries seem to be bad shots."

"Poor doves," Bringas said. "Those must have been the shots I heard this morning."

"They only killed a few, and they've given me three of those, three very plump birds. I tell you they are simply the best people in the world."

"There's no use telling me that," Bringas said. "It doesn't agree with what we know, it's nonsense. There's some mystery there. If what you say is true, then they aren't *canaille*, I repeat it, they aren't *canaille*, they are gentlemen—in disguise."

XLVII

When things had resumed their normal course again
and order had been restored in Madrid—not that it had
ever been much disturbed—the Committee took over
the Palace in due form and appointed custodians for it
and put a guard of soldiers there. Then the inhabitants of
the city upstairs could be at ease where their personal
safety was concerned; but they had other causes of
anxiety since they knew that they would soon be turned
out of what had become *The Palace of the Nation.*

Many of them began to intrigue to be allowed to
remain, while others, like Bringas, only wanted to show
their scorn of the revolution by leaving the apartments
which had ceased to be theirs as soon as possible. I had
the opportunity of becoming acquainted with the senti-
ments of every single inhabitant of the Palace on this
subject, for my luck—or my ill-fortune—had made me
the person chosen by the Committee to be the custodian
of the Colossus, and the administrator of the Crown
property contained in it. From the moment I was installed
in my office, the day wasn't long enough to listen to
the stories of all the distressed inhabitants of the Palace-
city. Some of them had to be left where they were
because of the position they occupied. The cleaners and
people who looked after the furniture and wardrobe-
keepers belonged to this category. Others provided subtle
reasons why they should not be forced to leave; and there
were even some who alleged revolutionary services as
a credential for becoming tenants of the Nation, as they
had formerly been tenants of the Monarchy. And all of
them brought letters of recommendation, from people

who had fallen or were going to fall, or from those who had risen or were going to rise. On these they based their requests for permanent lodgings or at any rate an extension of time before they had to move. The widow of Garcia Grande brought me such an appalling mass of cards and letters that rather than have to read them I allowed her to remain in her rooms as long as she liked.

I knew that Bringas wanted to leave immediately. But his wife came to see me to ask my permission for the family to remain in the Palace for a month while they were looking for an apartment—a request which I was only too glad to grant. Speaking of these extraordinary and unheard of events, the distinguished señora said to me that she did not look on the revolution with such implacable eyes as her husband did. She was confident that the Queen would come back—the Spaniards could never do without her—and in the meantime we must wait and see what happened before we passed judgment. Certainly things would be different, there would be new ways of life, different customs, and wealth would move from one section of the community to another. There would be great changes, no doubt, violent overthrows and sudden elevations, surprises, portents and that disorderly and irreflective movement of a society which has long been impatient for a change. From what the Señora de Bringas said to me—either in these words or very similar ones—I saw that the lady's imagination was full of the illusions of the unknown.

I wanted to show Bringas every consideration in my power, so I went myself to inform him that he could stay in his apartment as long as he wished to. But though he thanked me politely for my attention, he assured me that he was only anxious to leave as soon as possible: he did not want to owe any favours to the so-called Nation. Pez was with him and the three of us talked for

some time of the events of the day and of the Committee
and the Provisional Government which had just been
formed. Bringas was very much upset to find that Pez
was not as indignant as might have been expected from
his antecedants. But Pez defended himself in carefully
chosen language; judiciously holding up the theory of
the accomplished fact—the key both to politics and to
history.

"After all, what do you think we should do—spill
torrents of blood?" he said. "What has happened? Exactly what I have been saying for years would happen,
what I have been prophesying, what I have been announc-
ing. You have to bow your head before events and wait.
Wait and see what account these gentlemen give of
themselves."

Moreover, he believed that the presence of the Liberal
Union party in the Revolution was a guarantee against
its taking a dangerous path. He was quite tranquil, though
he was out of a job, and said to these Septembrists: "Now,
we'll see how you behave. I believe you'll do just the same
things we did, because the country isn't going to help
you, any more than it did us."

And what a happy chance it was that almost all the
men who composed the Committee were friends of Pez!
Some of them were actually relations, that is they belonged
to the great shoal of Peces in one way or another. He had
a number of friends and relatives in the Provisional
Government too. In fact wherever our friend turned his
eyes he encountered pisciform faces. And rather than
call such a state of things chance, let us call it the Philosophy of History.

My repeated urgings did not persuade Bringas to give
up his intention of vacating his apartment as soon as
possible. His wife, who came to thank me the day they
left, said that they had taken for the time being a very

humble apartment, but that they hoped to find something better soon, for she would not live in such a small shabby place, with more steps to climb than the tower of Santa Cruz. Bringas unemployed, Paquito unemployed! The situation was a cataclysm in the Bringuistic economy, and did not encourage ideas of grandeur. But the family must exert itself and not disgrace its traditional dignity and regard for proper appearances.

"In these critical circumstances," the Señora de Bringas said to me at the end of a long conversation, during which I fancied that she had favoured me with some rather provocative glances, "the fate of the family depends on me. I shall save it."

What she did to attain this end is something that does not lie within the scope of this narrative. But it may be definitely stated that in the years that followed the wife of Bringas understood how to triumph easily and even with a certain careless grace, over the difficulties into which her irregularities led her. It is an incontrovertible fact that she did not have nearly so much trouble in settling accounts with Refugio and getting rid of that repugnant fly, as she had had on previous similar occasions described in this book. The fact is that those occasions, intrigues, household dramas—or whatever you choose to call them— were the first trials of her changed moral state and found her still inexpert and, as it were, a novice.

I saw the departure of the Bringas family with real regret. The day they went, the upstairs city looked like a stronghold threatened with bombardment. Everyone there seemed to be leaving, and there was a confused passing to and fro of people and a colossal moving of furniture and household goods. It was impossible to get through the dim passage streets. Alfonsito enjoyed the spectacle to an extraordinary degree and longed to take charge of transporting everything—in his own carts.

But it was sad to see Don Francisco Bringas leaving the Palace. He walked slowly along, leaning on his wife's arm; his sight was much affected and he spoke with difficulty. Rosalía on the contrary walked serenely with something majestic in her carriage. She did not speak during the whole passage from their apartments to the Plaza de Oriente; but her eloquent eyes were full of a proud conviction, the consciousness of her role as corner-stone of the household in these tragic circumstances.

I learned what this meant in more precise terms from her own lips a little later, in a private interview. We were in the full revolutionary epoch by then. She seemed willing to repeat the proofs of her expensive friendship, but I did not encourage this idea. For, if it was natural that she should try to be the support of her unemployed family, I did not feel that I was called upon to aid her in it, against all laws of morality and domestic economy.

THE END

A LIST OF CHARACTERS

Don Francisco de Bringas a First Official of the Privy Purse living in the Royal Palace in Madrid.

Doña Rosalía Pipaón de la Barca, Señora de Bringas wife of the above. .

Paquito their son, a law student at the University.

Isabelita and *Alfonsito* their younger children.

Doña Milagros, the Marquesa de Tellería a friend of Rosalía's.

Maria, Leopold, Gustavo and *Luisito Sudre* children of Doña Milagros.

Doña Tula, the Condesa de Santa Barbara Doña Milagros' elder sister and a lady in waiting to Queen Isabella.

Doña Candida elderly and impoverished widow of *Señor Garcia Grande* once an important political figure.

Don Manuel Pez an important official in the Exchequer and the perfect type of bureaucrat. The word Pez means Fish and is chosen to signify the swarms of sinecure holders who live on the country.

Doña Carolina, Señora de Pez wife of the above. She is a *beata*, i.e. a woman who is intensely religious.

Refugio Sánchez Emperador a girl of doubtful character remotely connected with the Bringas family, by whom she and her sister *Amparo* had been rather unwillingly assisted.

Amparo had attracted the Bringas' rich cousin *Augustin Caballero* and gone off with him to Bordeaux.

Señor González Torres a man who places money for people and an old friend of the Bringas family.

Señor de Torquemada a money-lender.

Señor de Vargas a cashier in the office of the Privy Purse, where Bringas works.

Don Teodoro Golfín a famous oculist.

CPSIA information can be obtained at www.ICGtesting.com
Printed in the USA
LVOW13s0845290713

345110LV00003B/331/A